thegoodwebguide

travel

www.thegoodwebguide.co.uk

dedication

**For my family, Ian, Tom and George,
with all my love,
Emma**

thegoodwebguide

travel

Emma Burgess

The Good Web Guide Limited • London

First Published in Great Britain in 2000 by The Good Web Guide Limited
Broadwall House, 21 Broadwall, London, SE1 9PL

www.thegoodwebguide.co.uk

Email:feedback@thegoodwebguide.co.uk

Original series concept by Steve Bailey.

Cover photo © Macduff Everton/CORBIS

10 9 8 7 6 5 4 3 2 1

A catalogue record for this book is available from the British Library.

ISBN 1-903282-05-5

Project Editor Michelle Clare

Design by Myriad Creative Ltd

Printed in Italy at LEGO S.p.A.

How to use your CD

Once you have read the sites reviewed in this book, we can help you to visit them quickly and easily. By registering on thegoodwebguide site, you will be able to use the hotlinks to all the sites listed, so you just click and go. You can also read the latest versions of reviews and see what we think of new sites that have been launched since the book went to press. If you wish, you can even have the updates emailed to you.

INSTALLATION INSTRUCTIONS FOR PC USERS
Insert the CD enclosed with this book into your CD drive of your PC. A welcome screen will appear with two buttons:

The goodwebguide button To register your purchase of a Good Web Guide book and to receive free updates of the reviews in the book and reviews of the latest sites, click on this button. When you've registered you can click straight through to any of the sites listed. You must have an internet connection to do this. If you are not already signed up with an internet service, you will need to install the LineOne software first.

If you click on the goodwebguide button you will be taken to a registration page where you will be asked to confirm which title in the series you have bought and to register your details. You then have free access to the updates of the website reviews in this book and to new reviews. You will also have access to the rest of the goodwebguide website.

LineOne button If you would like access to the internet you can click on this button to install LineOne's free ISP (internet service provider) software. You will need a modem to have internet access. If you already have an internet connection

(ISP) you can still install LineOne as an alternative provider.

A To join LineOne just click on the LineOne button. When the first screen appears you have a choice: If you are a new user and wish to load Internet Explorer 5 as your browser, select 'Join Now'. On the next screen, select 'Go!' and you will be taken to the Microsoft installation process.

B To join immediately, without installing a browser, click 'Join Now' and then choose 'custom' to go straight to registration.

From the 'Welcome to LineOne' screen, click 'Go' and follow the on-screen instructions.

MAC USERS
This CD is not suitable for Apple Macintosh computers. For Free LineOne Mac Software call free on 0800 111 210.

RETURNING TO THE GOOD WEB GUIDE
Once you've connected to the internet, you can either type www.thegoodwebguide.co.uk into your browser to go directly to our website, or re-insert your CD and click on the goodwebguide button.

SUPPORT
If you have any problems call the LineOne support number.
CALL 0906 30 20 100
(calls may be monitored or recorded for training purposes) 24 hours, 365 days a year. Calls charged at 50p/minute or email support@lineone.net for free support.

contents

the good web guides

The World Wide Web is a vast resource, with millions of sites on every conceivable subject. There are people who have made it their mission to surf the net: cyber-communities have grown, and people have formed relationships and even married on the net.

However, the reality for most people is that they don't have the time or inclination to surf the net for hours on end. Busy people want to use the internet for quick access to information. You don't have to spend hours on the internet looking for answers to your questions and you don't have to be an accomplished net surfer or cyber wizard to get the most out of the web. It can be a quick and useful resource if you are looking for specific information.

The Good Web Guides have been published with this in mind. To give you a head start in your search, our researchers have looked at hundreds of sites and what you will find in the Good Web Guides is a collection of reviews of the best we've found.

The Good Web Guide recommendation is impartial and all the sites have been visited several times. Reviews are focused on the website and what it sets out to do, rather than an endorsement of a company, or their product. A small but beautiful site run by a one-man band may be rated higher than an ambitious but flawed site run by a mighty organisation.

Relevance to the UK-based visitor is also given a high premium: tantalising as it is to read about purchases you can make in California, because of delivery charges, import duties and controls it may not be as useful as a local site.

Our reviewers considered a number of questions when reviewing the sites, such as: How quickly do the sites and individual pages download? Can you move around the site easily and get back to where you started, and do the links work? Is the information up to date and accurate? And is the site pleasing to the eye and easy to read? More importantly, we also asked whether the site has something distinctive to offer, whether it be entertainment, inspiration or pure information. On the basis of the answers to these questions sites are given ratings out of five. As we aim only to include sites that we feel are of serious interest, there are very few low-rated sites.

Bear in mind that the collection of reviews you see here are just a snapshot of the sites at a particular time. The process of choosing and writing about sites is rather like painting the Forth Bridge: as each section appears complete, new sites are launched and others are modified. When you've registered at the Good Web Guide site (see p. 5 for further details) you can check out the reviews of new sites and updates of existing ones, or even have them emailed to you. By using the cd rom at the back of the book or registering at our site, you'll find hot links to all the sites listed, so you can just click and go without needing to type the addresses accurately into your browser.

As this is the first edition of the Good Web Guide, all our sites have been reviewed by the author and research team, but we'd like to know what you think. Contact us via the website or email feedback@thegoodwebguide.co.uk. You are welcome to recommend sites, quibble about the ratings, point out changes and inaccuracies or suggest new features to assess.

You can find us at www.thegoodwebguide.co.uk

user key

 £   Subscription Required

 R   Registration Required

     Secure Online Ordering

 UK   Country of origin

introduction

Online travel is the largest ecommerce category on the internet. With its sudden explosion in Britain recently, it has become a chaotic and frenzied industry in which to partake, whether as consumer or player. Every Travel Tom who has anything remotely relevant to say, or do, about travel, is starting a website. For the general consumer, all this www stuff can be very confusing. Where do you start?

Let's begin by setting out the players – those with websites. Basically, there are three categories: those who were involved in the travel reservations systems (the technology was used by travel agents prior to the development of the World Wide Web); those who had recognised brand names in the travel sector, for example, British Airways, or the tour operator Kuoni; and, finally, the entrepreneurial generic dot.coms, who had no experience with the sector, but were more advanced in website language and had the foresight to see that the travel business suits the internet.

There are many reasons why travel complements the internet so well. For the players, or companies, with websites who hope to profit from them in some way, whether financially or through exposure, the internet can work well as an additional platform. First, the transactional nature of the industry lends itself to the web: apart from tickets, there is very little physical product to deliver to consumers. Furthermore, companies that traditionally rely on commission-taking agents can improve their margins by cutting out the middle man.

For the consumer, there are obvious advantages in planning a holiday or researching a city from the comfort of your own home or office; you have the added advantages of being in control and well informed. Talking to agents across a desk, or on the telephone, and getting the impression that they are giving you selected bits of advice from the mysterious system on their computer screen is a thing of the past. Now you can see for yourself exactly what is on offer, how many flights there are for a specific route, or where that seat is in the plane. And, if you peruse a brochure online, you can then print out chosen sections rather than waiting for the full encyclopaedia-size transcript to arrive by post.

Consumers are hoping that the cost benefit of cutting out the agents will be passed on to them, resulting in cheaper accommodation, transport and overall travel costs. The travel industry is information heavy, traditionally relying on bulky brochures to provide details and prices. The invention of the web has removed the need for such publications as consumers can search and compile their own personal catalogues on screen.

With a perfect alliance of benefits for the consumer and the operators, the future of travel on the web seems assured. It's still too early to tell which players will survive the frenzy and maintain long-term presence and success, but one thing is certain: those players who already have established brand names have an enormous advantage. This is becoming a brand business entailing high costs, and it will definitely result in some misfortunes. Website founders and investors have already seen that management styles must mature from the overly keen, aggressive entrepreneurs to marketeers with a strong sense of control. The travel industry is evolving fast and teething problems will soon be wiped out with prices coming down.

The future promises further exciting developments, with versions of web technologies delivered via digital TVs and WAP mobile phones. Soon, you may be able to go through the checking-in process from a taxi or from your computer at work before you actually reach the airport.

Even now, the information available on the web is massive, and there is more than anyone could ever have hoped to have at his or her fingertips. In such a fast-changing industry, the websites featured on the following pages can only hope to be a snapshot of the best available at the time of writing. Follow these suggestions and you'll be able to do everything from researching far-off destinations and cultures to pin-pointing the exact location of a cash machine. You can book a standard package holiday at a discount or create a bespoke tour. Most of the sites listed here are likely to be key players in the long-term, but changes are inevitable; some will expand their services, merge with others, fall by the wayside, or be overtaken by new players. Throughout all of this, you will have access to the latest news and reviews by registering at www.thegoodwebguide.co.uk to receive your free online updates.

So, sit down and use the following pages to help you enjoy it. There's a whole world of travel out there, and with the web attached, it is not one to fear.

Emma Burgess, June 2000

Chapter 1

travel destinations

'For also knowledge itself is power.'

Francis Bacon (1597)

One of the best and most rewarding uses of the web is to research travel destinations. Information is available on countries, regions, or specific cities, whether they are in remotest Africa or close to home.

The quantity and quality of detail available are astounding. As well as providing information, surfing the travel guide pages can be as pleasurable as reading a good book. With screen graphics of zebras in the Mala Mala Game Reserve or Bilbao's Guggenheim Museum, even the dullest British evening can be brightened up.

The following sites are useful for those with a trip already planned, those who need inspiration for their next holiday, or for purely recreational browsing.

They are divided geographically by continent, and are the very best on the web. Sites relating to travel within the

United Kingdom come first, followed by sites which refer to travel in several different regions. Sites relating to individual continents come after this and are arranged in alphabetical order.

The list is compiled with the intention of steering the visitor directly to the desired location without making any wrong turns, since losing one's way on the web is just as frustrating as it is in real-life travel.

United Kingdom

www.tour-britain.com
Tour Britain

Overall rating: ★ ★ ★ ★			
Classification:	Information	**Readability:**	★ ★ ★ ★ ★
Updating:	Daily	**Content:**	★ ★ ★ ★
Navigation:	★ ★ ★ ★	**Speed:**	★ ★ ★
UK			

Tour Britain is an ambitious project, which is still under construction and rather slow to load. It's an international online booking service for flights, cars and hotels, and is also a one-stop travel guide for all things British.

It's a shame the homepage doesn't always load smoothly, but the title band strip makes navigation easy by listing the main categories: Travel, Entertainment, Shop, Guides, Top Places and Resources.

SPECIAL FEATURES

Guides on any of the 40 areas in England can be bought for £5, but online payment isn't available and it's necessary to send a cheque via snail mail. Brochures on Wales and Scotland are also mentioned.

Travel is divided into four clear and easily navigable sections. Flights, rail tickets, coaches and ferries can be booked in Transport, and Accommodation highlights hotels, mostly British, but a few international. Top Holidays is divided into special interests, and there's a section on Top UK Tours.

Entertainment, Top Places and Resources aren't yet functioning.

A few teething problems still need to be overcome, but can be largely forgiven at this stage as this site promises to be a crown jewel.

www.travel-library.com/europe/uk/
Travel Library

Overall rating: ★ ★ ★ ★			
Classification:	Information	**Readability:**	★ ★ ★ ★ ★
Updating:	Various	**Content:**	★ ★ ★
Navigation:	★ ★ ★ ★ ★	**Speed:**	★ ★ ★ ★ ★

US

This site is aimed mostly at the visitor from outside the UK, but it can be equally helpful to Brits planning a long weekend away from home. Operating like the index to books in a library, this unfussy site gives an index of links which cover many subjects relating to the UK.

The homepage concentrates on the UK as a whole, providing links to Tour Operators, Travelogues or Regional Information. The visitor with a more exact query, however, may be better served linking to the individual pages for England, Ireland, Scotland or Wales.

The pages for all four countries are presented in the same, simple-to-use way, with the largest heading of **Regional Information** providing the most links underneath. Here, information is provided via links to the official websites of local tourist boards and county councils. The second largest category is **Travelogues**; the final two other categories of **Accommodation** and **Tour Operators,** and **Travel Agents**, have comparatively fewer links.

As this is a site dependent on links, the quality of information can vary slightly, but, in general, it is fairly comprehensive and of a high standard.

Worldwide

www.about.com/travel
About.com

Overall rating: ★★★★★			
Classification: Information		**Readability:** ★★★★	
Updating: Monthly		**Content:** ★★★	
Navigation: ★★★		**Speed:** ★★★	

US

About.com is essentially an online directory which aims to differentiate itself by using expert guides to turn up only the really good stuff. It's part of a network of over 700 sites, covering many special interest topics. This main travel site is a point of entry to over 80 sites hosted by the network, covering continents and countries, types of travel and accommodation, special interest holidays, culture and language. Each site is hosted by its own expert guide, and is full of links and articles. If you are looking for very specific information, you may find it quicker to use the Find It Now and Go facilities to get the most from the site.

SPECIAL FEATURES

Get to the Site You Want monopolises the two left-hand columns of the homepage, and gives direct links to all the travel sites. These include specific countries and even cities, camping, skiing and other adventure holidays, honeymoons, ecotourism and travelling with kids. Each site lists other related sites, and has a good archive of articles.

Expert Insight on Travel is by far the best section of this general site. Each month two new articles are added on speciality travel-related subjects, such as baking with a

Dutch oven for campers, or the coyotes of Mexico. Scroll down to the bottom of each article to find a link to three-years-worth of previous features, archived by date.

Shopping is a general section covering the entire site, with a directory of over 40,000 stores. Everything from antiques to video games is offered, including, fortunately, a travel section. It's possible to personalise your shopping experience by creating a list of frequently visited stores. Take heed: when exiting your favourites page, back page with your browser, or run the risk of facing a jungle of shops blocking your way back.

OTHER FEATURES

Talk About gives a list of chat rooms, which, unfortunately, seem to be mostly drivel-ridden. **Resource** covers only Africa, Mexico and Europe, an odd combination, and leads to the same sites and links as the Get to the Site You Want categories. The purpose of this redundant feature isn't clear.

The site can offer information on almost any aspect of travel, but, as with any search facility, getting there can be frustrating and the final result occasionally disappointing.

www.timeout.com
Time Out

Overall rating: ★ ★ ★ ★			
Classification:	Information	Readability:	★ ★ ★ ★ ★
Updating:	Monthly	Content:	★ ★ ★ ★ ★
Navigation:	★ ★ ★ ★ ★	Speed:	★ ★ ★ ★ ★

UK

Time Out is part guide to the world's biggest cities and part beckoning finger, and it is fantastic. For those travelling to one of the 50 cities covered by Time Out reviews, a wealth of detailed information is given on accommodation, entertainment, eating, drinking and sightseeing.

The site is a navigational dream as it is so smooth and easy. Subtitled The World's Living Guide, it provides urban coverage only. It is not directed at those seeking a bucolically inclined holiday, but deserves three cheers for sticking to what it does best.

SPECIAL FEATURES

City Links directs visitors to Time Out's selection of hottest links for each city. This is the sign of a site with confidence, unafraid that links to other sites will show it up.

Currency Converter is perhaps not used that often but is handy, and should our maths checks serve us correctly, accurate.

Travel Booking links to Microsoft's online travel agency, Expedia (see p. 41).

An entertaining site producing reliable, quality information.

www.traveldex.co.uk
TravelDex

Overall rating: ★ ★ ★ ★ ★			
Classification:	Information	**Readability:**	★ ★ ★ ★ ★
Updating:	Various	**Content:**	★ ★ ★ ★
Navigation:	★ ★ ★ ★ ★	**Speed:**	★ ★ ★ ★

UK

Oh the beauty of simplicity! With one of the most straightforward homepages on the web (the Traveldex logo and names of six continents in red on a white background), visitors can link quickly to regional information. In short, it's a specialist destination search engine and a fantastic starting point. The only drawback is that under many of the countries there isn't any information yet, but for African regions and holiday spot islands, such as those in the Caribbean, a visit would be worthwhile.

SPECIAL FEATURES

Country Information gives links to websites providing cultural information such as the geography and climate of the country and other tourist board-type information.

Holidays provides links to the websites of less well-known, but interesting, tour operators. A lot of them seem geared towards organising custom-made trips. Others cater for the alternative traveller, for example, those wishing to travel the world on a motorbike. Some countries list only one entry whereas Mexico, for example, lists five.

Accommodation again links to other sites that vary in size and content. Some links here are to specific hotels while others are to all-encompassing regional hotel directories.

Travel Advice is supposed to link to the UK's Foreign and Commonwealth Office's Travel Advice page, but the URL appears to have the word Travel missing from the address, so the link is unsuccessful. Hopefully, the site designers will soon remedy this problem but, until then, you can visit www.fco.gov.uk/travel/countryadvice.asp for travel advice.

Currency offers two alternatives: the Interactive Currency Converter, which allows the inputting of a currency, an amount and a currency to convert into, and The Universal Currency Converter, where one chooses a currency with a date, and a table is produced of the value of that currency in many other currencies worldwide.

Tourist Attractions and Getting Around sound like interesting categories, but, unfortunately, there don't appear to be any links to them so far.

This site is most useful for those with a destination already in mind; while its graphics make for easy reading and smooth navigation, they don't necessarily inspire. This site is there to give information, which it does in abundance if you ignore the occasional bald patches in the links.

OTHER SITES OF INTEREST

Tourism Offices Worldwide Directory

www.towd.com

A marvellously easy-to-use directory listing 1,674 official government tourism offices, bureaux, chambers of commerce and similar agencies. A drop-down menu allows you to link to any office in the directory that has a website. This should be the first port of call for anyone travelling to a new destination. Although it has a slight US bias, it is very handy and there are few navigational hurdles.

Travel Library

http://rec.travelmate.com

The European arm of the well-known US Travel Library, this site provides quality and easy-to-find tourist information, personal travelogues and trip reports.

Travel Source

www.travelsource.com

Travel Source claims to be the internet's first interactive travel guide featuring unique travel destinations and adventure vacations worldwide. (See also p. 69)

World Tour Guides

www.world-tour-guides.aust.com

Supplies real-life, personal tour guides around the world. You must be specific with requests, such as 60+, middle-aged or toy boy!

Expedia.com (see p. 41)

www.expedia.msn.com/wg

Travel Notes.Org

www.travelnotes.org

My Travel Guide.com

www.mytravelguide.com

wcities.com

www.wcities.com

Guide Books Online

Lonely Planet

www.lonelyplanet.com

Rough Guide

http://travel.roughguides.com

Fodors.com

www.fodors.com

Footprint Books

www.footprintbooks.com

Lets Go

www.letsgo.com

Arthur Frommer's Budget Travel Online

www.frommers.com

Africa

This online travel guide to Africa currently has very detailed information on Namibia but only basic information on all other African countries. The site plans to offer comprehensive, in-depth information on all countries as well as online reservation capabilities and a library of travel writing. The site is well-laid-out and it looks like this will become the ultimate online guide to Africa.

SPECIAL FEATURES

Gallery presents beautiful pictures of wildlife, scenery, people and flora from many African countries. Great to send to others before or after a trip, or you can download some zebras as a screen saver.

Sport covers information on anything and everything there is to know about African football teams, the players, results and matches. There is an extensive archive, so fans should be prepared to spend some time here.

Health is a comprehensive guide to the tragic aids epidemic and the disease's spread through Africa. There is information and statistics by region as well as recent articles on the subject.

On the whole, an extensive and extremely creative site for the traveller. As well as the categories listed above, there's full and comprehensive information to ensure a smooth visit.

OTHER SITES OF INTEREST

A Brief Guide to Africa
www.africa.co.uk/country/af-guide.htm

As part of the Africa Today venture to promote business and interest in Africa, this page offers links to socio-economic information for each country. Not particularly inspiring but it provides the basic data.

My Travel Guide.com
www.mytravelguide.com/africa.asp?corridor=

Lexic Orient
http://I-cias.com

Visit Kenya
www.visit-kenya.com

Africa Online
www.africaonline.co.ke

Egyptian Tourist Authority
www.touregypt.net

Gambia Net
www.gambianet.com

Kenya Web
www.kenyaweb.com

Morocco Bound
http://tayara.com/club/mrocbd1.htm

Mauritius Tourism Promotion Agency
www.mauritius.net

Sudan Net
www.sudan.net

Zanzibar.net
www.zanzibar.net

Southern Africa Places
www.places.co.za

Tourism in Swaziland
www.swazi.com/tourism

North America

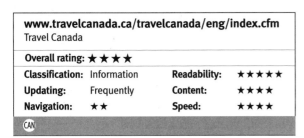

www.travelcanada.ca/travelcanada/eng/index.cfm
Travel Canada

Overall rating: ★ ★ ★ ★			
Classification:	Information	**Readability:**	★ ★ ★ ★ ★
Updating:	Frequently	**Content:**	★ ★ ★ ★
Navigation:	★ ★	**Speed:**	★ ★ ★ ★

CAN

This is the Canadian Tourist Commission site for English-speaking visitors. It's good, but not excellent, and promises to give the visitor all the information needed to plan a trip. The attractively-designed homepage divides itself into Travel Guides, Things To Do and Places To Go. There's also a section on Canadian trivia: for example, 'did you know that the glass floor at the top of the world's tallest free-standing structure can support the weight of 14 hippos?'

SPECIAL FEATURES

Virtual Tour invites you to Let Yourself Go in Canada, and a series of scenic photographs can be selected and viewed from a regional menu, although the technology needs a little improvement to make it more rewarding.

Before You Travel is very informative and answers a whole bunch of questions about getting to Canada, entry requirements, together with plenty of other practical information. It should be the first point of call for anyone travelling to Canada.

Overall, a very informative site, even if presentation and logic are a little wacky.

www.usa.com
America's Home Page

Overall rating: ★ ★ ★			
Classification:	Directory	**Readability:**	★ ★ ★
Updating:	Frequently	**Content:**	★ ★ ★ ★
Navigation:	★ ★	**Speed:**	★ ★

US

Although it can sometimes seem overwhelming, this site houses every sort of information imaginable about people, places and things in the US. It's particularly strong on phone books and business listings.

Each page operates using the same fill-in-the-blanks type format. Beyond that, there are links to click on and very few pictures taking up space.

SPECIAL FEATURES

Places is a fantastic facility. No need to run out of the special film required for that ancient camera! By entering a business type, such as a photo lab, and the name of a town, however small, all holiday needs can easily be met. This page also offers international telephone directories.

Slide Show, hidden at the bottom of the Places search page, is a delightfully artistic summons to places of interest in the US. The pictures are so vivid that you begin to question whether sitting in a metal tube and breathing in re-circulated, bug-ridden air for eight hours is really necessary.

People turns up addresses and public records (for a $10 fee) for anyone and everyone that you might want to visit. Look up all those exes!

Web is yet another search engine. You can search under Automotive, Business and Finance, Computers and Internet, Entertainment and Media, Home & Family, Shopping &

Services, Sports and Recreation, Travel and Vacations in order to be linked to different, specialist search sites.

Shop Talk is interesting for everyone remaining in the UK who may be interested in purchasing American products. With its link to an extensive shopping search facility, it's possible to buy any item imaginable, or join a chat room to discuss them.

Reverse Listings, featured quite obviously on the homepage, lets you input a US or Canadian telephone number and it will reveal the identity of the person behind the number. Its position of importance on the site leads you to believe that it must be frequently put to use!

Free Home Pages, listed under the people category, is a hidden gem, not necessarily for those researching the US, but for those who have always wanted to build their own web page. It offers one of the most comprehensive step-by-step guides to making and registering a website. Excellent for those making this a rainy day weekend project with the children.

This site is great for those looking for a specific person, place or thing, although some other sites are better suited for those researching the big picture.

www.usatourist.com
USATourist

Overall rating: ★ ★ ★			
Classification:	Information	**Readability:**	★ ★ ★ ★
Updating:	Frequently	**Content:**	★ ★ ★ ★
Navigation:	★ ★	**Speed:**	★ ★ ★ ★

US

With a picture of the Statue of Liberty and the Star Spangled Banner flapping patriotically, this large site aims to give foreign tourists an insight into the US, and all the information required for travelling there. It needs a search facility to be really useful, though, as certain obvious subjects, such as Boston, can't be found anywhere. It's a Net Nanny-approved site, although it perhaps loses something by attempting to please everyone. That said, the homepage and following pages are easy to navigate, following the American format of fewer graphics. Scroll down to make sure you don't miss anything as not all the categories appear at first glance.

SPECIAL FEATURES

USA Tourist Partners, on the left-hand side of the homepage, has links to visitor brochures and discount coupons, home exchange information, hotel and car reservations, and an especially interesting link for bikers, who can rent Harley Davidsons from a company called Eagle Rider.

Inside USA gives some historical, geographical and cultural information on sport, cowboys, native Americans, and seasonal sightseeing, but lacks any really pertinent detail.

Cool Places gives information on selected tourist locations, such as Las Vegas and Florida, with helpful tips for visitors.

US Parks is one of the fullest categories with pages on every type of park in the United States, from theme parks such as Disney to all the natural phenomena like Niagara Falls, Bryce Canyon National Park and Monument Valley.

USA Adventures gives details of adventure trips in places such as the Grand Canyon and Death Valley.

Hot Tips gives insider information on travel, from planes to hitchhiking, budget accommodation, food, shopping and personal safety.

Market Place presents two categories of Bookstore and Hotel Reservations. Bookstore links to Amazon.com (the American site), while Hotel Reservations links to a very successful search facility and Travelnow.com. This site presents a comprehensive quality hotel search with booking online. It also offers the added bonus of rental car booking capabilities.

There's a fair amount of useful background information about the United States on this site, but for detailed holiday planning, use alternative resources.

For a list of sites relating to individual states enter the state of your choice at the end of the following URL: http://travel.yahoo.com/Destinations/North_America/Countries/United_States/

Caribbean

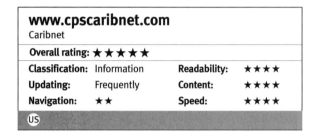

www.cpscaribnet.com
Caribnet

Overall rating: ★ ★ ★ ★			
Classification:	Information	**Readability:**	★ ★ ★ ★
Updating:	Frequently	**Content:**	★ ★ ★ ★
Navigation:	★ ★	**Speed:**	★ ★ ★ ★
US			

This five-star site acts as a gateway to the Caribbean. A couple of balmy-looking snapshots on the homepage give a tempting taste of a dream holiday, which is surprisingly easy to research and plan with the help of the site. Navigation is simple, with a scroll-down menu on the left-hand side of the homepage. Strangely, the menu begins with the site's weakest page, Headline News.

Destinations gives a virtual tour of any Caribbean island. Starting with a simple map, you can choose to find out more about Information and History, Real Estate (in the event that you've had enough with merry old England), or Sites and Side Trips.

Accommodation gives a choice of Inns & Hideaways, or Luxury Resorts, but the problem is quantity: there's not enough to choose from.

Dolphin Encounters is slightly misleading as it relates only to the Bahamas and not to the Caribbean as a whole, but if you're in Nassau, these day trips sound interesting.

A handy site for information, even if the organisational logic isn't always clear.

OTHER SITES OF INTEREST

Rec.Travel Library
www.travel-library.com/caribbean
The Caribbean pages of this site are just one section of a vast travel library. Information on the region is eclectic and includes links to a wide range of sites on the Caribbean. There's also a sizeable amout of information available on tour operators, travel agents and accommodation.

Latin America

www.centralamerica.com
Costa Rica's Travel Net

Overall rating: ★ ★ ★ ★

Classification:	Agent	Readability:	★ ★ ★ ★ ★
Updating:	Frequently	Content:	★ ★ ★ ★
Navigation:	★ ★ ★ ★ ★	Speed:	★ ★ ★ ★

US

Travel Net tour operators host these three useful and fairly impartial sites on Costa Rica, Nicaragua and Panama. They are well laid-out and easy to use, with many links to popular local hotels and travel businesses of all kinds. Daily tours to sightseeing attractions can be booked directly as well as multi-day holiday tours in the area. There is also a big plug for the services of Travel Net.

The main site covers everything Costa Rican, and is divided into three main sections.

SPECIAL FEATURES

Learn a Little gives background cultural information, maps, descriptions of the region's national parks and information on the first Costa Rican butterfly farm!

Home Pages lists hotels, car rentals, local flights, nature and adventure tours.

Special Interest gives lots of information on all kinds of adventure holidays, from rafting to scuba diving and surfing.

Fundación Ríos Tropicales gives information about how a private, non-profit organisation is working to keep Central America's environment green.

There are links to the sites on Nicaragua and Panama from the main page, and these are laid out even more efficiently, with an abundance of general information and details of tourist areas, packages and hotels.

Three sites not to be missed for anyone considering a trip to this part of the world.

www.latinamericatraveler.com
Latin America Traveler

Overall rating: ★ ★ ★ ★

Classification:	Information	**Readability:**	★ ★ ★ ★
Updating:	Frequently	**Content:**	★ ★ ★
Navigation:	★ ★ ★ ★	**Speed:**	★ ★ ★ ★

(US)

Covering both Central America and South America, this site intends to be the starting point for anyone interested in Latin American countries. Use the 'links' menu to select your country of choice from the graphically mellow and easy-to-use homepage. Once on the new page, scroll down to the Tourism category, trying not to get side-tracked by all the interesting links on the way, to link to the best travel information available for the region. Unfortunately, not all of these links were live at time of review.

SPECIAL FEATURES

Things You should Know is an excellent education source and provides at least 32 basic pieces of historic, geographic or cultural information about South America. It's a must for anyone who doesn't want to look or sound like a complete 'head in the sands' on a first visit.

Security Reports are issued only after a $15 cheque has been received by the Crowder Travel Company (the site's backers), so best to give this feature a miss.

Spanish Schools offers those linguists who hope to master another language a range of holidays or other study possibilities.

OTHER SITES OF INTEREST

About.com Travel

www.gosouthamerica.about.com/

Masses of information for travellers in South America, resulting in a crowded, but not unworkable, homepage. If you really like to do your homework before you go, then this is the place to find out about subjects as diverse as current affairs, festivals and environmental issues.

Nicaragua's Travel Net

www.centralamerica.com/nicaragua/index.htm

Another instalment from the Travelnet group, this time covering countries in Central America, in the form of an online travel guide. There's plenty of practical information, including bank opening hours, maps and emergency medical services.

Panama's Travel Net

www.centralamerica.com/panama/index.htm

Central America.com

www.centralamerica.com/costarica/index.htm

Travel.org

www.travel.org/latin

Travel Latin America

www.travellatinamerica.com

Planeta.com: Ecotravels in Latin America

www.planeta.com

Asia

www.asiatravel.com
Asia Travel

Overall rating: ★ ★ ★			
Classification:	Agent	**Readability:**	★★★★
Updating:	Real time	**Content:**	★★★
Navigation:	★★★★	**Speed:**	★★★★★

HK

This Asian hotel and resorts reservation service boasts up to 75 per cent discount for an online reservation. The site is simple and well designed, and gives comprehensive factual information on hotels and resorts as well as air ticket, country and sight-seeing advice for over 20 countries. The site is indexed by geographical location and is best suited for those travelling for recreation rather than business.

SPECIAL FEATURES

Travel Information gives comprehensive general information about the usual subjects, such as geography and climate, but also goes on to give fairly worthwhile cultural information on such topics as how people expect to be greeted in business and the immense value of giving small gifts. Well worth the time spent browsing.

Hotels and resort details are broken down into groups by price in US dollars, so make sure your exchange rate is correct to prevent a costly mistake.

Tours, Sightseeing and Excursions is less developed than the hotel and travel information, so it's probably best to stick to those two categories.

Electronic Postcards of some rather predictable tourist highlights are available on each country's page, and are easy to send.

Best used as an insight to accommodation possibilities.

www.asia.com
Asia.com

Overall rating: ★ ★ ★			
Classification:	Information	**Readability:**	★ ★ ★ ★
Updating:	Frequently	**Content:**	★ ★ ★ ★
Navigation:	★ ★ ★ ★	**Speed:**	★ ★ ★ ★

CH

Formed in March 2000, Asia.com is a network of sites serving the Greater China area, Korea, Thailand and Singapore. It's a well-laid-out site with good graphics, and, despite the severe colour scheme, promises good things.

Currently, however, only the China section is up and running, with the promise that Hong Kong, Korea, Singapore and Thailand will follow imminently.

OTHER SITES OF INTEREST

Mytravelguide
www.mytravelguide.com/asia.asp?corridor=

India Online
www.tourindia.com

Cambodia Web
www.cambodia-web.net

Hong Kong.com
http://english.hongkong.com/hkdc/en

Fil Info
www.filipino.com

Travel Japan
www.jtb.co.jp/TJsote/index-e.html

Bali Paradise Online
www.bali-paradise.com

Asia Tour
www.asiatour.com

Vietnam Traveling
www.vietnamtraveling.com/main.html

Welcome to Korea
www.knto.or.kr/english/index.html

Australasia

www.global.australia.com
www.global.australia.com

Overall rating: ★ ★ ★ ★			
Classification: Information		**Readability:**	★ ★ ★ ★ ★
Updating: Frequently		**Content:**	★ ★ ★ ★
Navigation: ★ ★ ★ ★ ★		**Speed:**	★ ★ ★ ★ ★

AUS

The Australian Tourist Commission offers 10,000 pages of searchable information for planning and researching a holiday. It's the gateway to Australian tourist information about cities, regions, culture, activities, products and events. It also links to specialist Aussie travel agents. Unbelievably for such a large site, it is easily navigated from a visually distinct and inviting main menu on the homepage.

SPECIAL FEATURES

Why Holiday in Australia is great for convincing a potential travel companion that it's worth the long haul.

Special Interests should be your first stop if you've decided that you might like to visit Australia. It gives an extensive alphabetical menu of interests, spanning four-wheel drives, the outback, food and wine and camel trekking.

Frequently Asked Questions is a carefully put-together list of responses to the 24 most commonly asked questions. A quick browse through this and Facts for the Visitor gives good preparation for departure.

For those who have never considered travelling to Australia, a visit to this site may spur a change of heart.

Europe

www.4Europe.com			
4Europe			
Overall rating: ★ ★ ★ ★			
Classification: Information		**Readability:**	★ ★ ★ ★ ★
Updating: Daily		**Content:**	★ ★ ★ ★
Navigation: ★ ★ ★ ★		**Speed:**	★ ★ ★ ★ ★
US			

Part of the 4Anything network, 4Europe gives information on 5,000 destinations worldwide. Although it describes itself as a guide to Europe, all links revert back to a worldwide network. The European information, however, is of excellent quality.

The site has a slight US bias, with a homepage that is somewhat overcrowded and illogical, but after emerging from it, navigation is easy. The bulk of the information can be found in Travel Spots, which is the second topic listed in the Destinations and Tours menu.

SPECIAL FEATURES

Destinations gives an exhaustive alphabetical list of geographical locations. Using a scroll-down menu you find the location of choice and then retrieve links to quality sites.

Holiday Types presents an all-inclusive scroll-down menu of special interest holidays. Everything from bird-watching to tennis is included, but if you're looking for something more unpredictable, take a look at Wild Stuff. You'll be presented with an abundance of information on a wide range of interests including Adrift Adventures, Bungee Jumping, Trekking and Whale Watching.

Listings saves visitors from having to exit the site to look for further information. It links to a collection of major airlines, airports, cruise lines, hotels and car companies, and although it's a US site, there doesn't appear to be a US bias.

Travel Stuff links visitors to sites of any travel-related information, from currency to health. It's US Government agency information, and is therefore slightly heavy on American organisations.

Fun allows travel enthusiasts to do such things as send emails and listen to radio stations. It is especially useful for sending an epostcard to friends before you set off (or after returning, when you wish you'd sent one). By clicking on Postcards and then Create Your Own, a mass of kitsch-looking images appears, but by clicking on Picture Search some fairly tasteful images can be selected. There are also Recipes from Around the World, high quality screen savers, and Travel Biorhythms.

Reserve is ever so slightly misleading. In reality it gives visitors the opportunity to register so that a travel agent in the area may (or may not, as it would appear) contact them.

This has got to be one of the best travel sites available. It has a lot to offer without being too overwhelming.

www.travel-library.com/europe
Travel Library

Overall rating: ★ ★ ★ ★			
Classification:	Information	**Readability:**	★ ★ ★ ★ ★
Updating:	Frequently	**Content:**	★ ★ ★ ★ ★
Navigation:	★ ★ ★ ★	**Speed:**	★ ★ ★ ★ ★

US

One of the best sites from which to take the plunge into European tourist information.

The layout is boring, and the blue-on-blue graphics don't make a lot of sense, but, as with a town hall library, the information can always be found with a little effort. It's directed slightly more to the budget tourist than the luxury traveller. For quick and easy navigation, avoid the never-ending scroll-down menu on the homepage and use the drop-down search-and-go menu at the top.

SPECIAL FEATURES

Travelogues presents articles on many aspects of travel in Europe dating back to 1990. The content varies from wacky to pertinent, and is always interesting.

The library offers a comprehensive list of European destinations. Don't miss this site.

OTHER SITES OF INTEREST

Global Online Directory
www.god.co.uk
This links site covers a comprehensive range of travel-related
subjects, from accommodation to personal travelogues.

Austrian Tourist Guide
www.abserv.co.at/abserv/tourist

Living in Belgium
www.living-in-belgium.com

Brussels.com
www.brussels.com

Bulgarian Travel Guide
www.travel-bulgaria.com

Central Europe Online
www.centraleurope.com/travel

Cyprus Tourism
www.cyprustourism.org

Czech Tourism Page
www.czech-tourism.com

Danish Tourist Board
www.dt.dk

In Your Pocket - Eastern & Central Europe
www.inyourpocket.com

Virtual Finland
http://virtual.finland.fi

Tourism in France
www/tourisme.fr/us/index.htm

German Tourist Board
www.germany-tourism.de

Greek National Tourism Operation
www.areianet.gr/infoxenios

Greek Ionian Islands
www.ionian-islands.com

Welcome to Holland
www.visitholland.com

Icelandic Tourist Board
www.icetourist.is

Access Ireland
www.visunet.ie/anlysses.htm

In Italy Online
www.initaly.com

Luxembourg Tourist Office
www.luxembourg.co.uk

Malta Tourism Authority
www.visitmalta.com

Monaco
www.monaco.mc/monaco/index.html

Société des Bains de Mer
www.montecarloresort.com

Norwegian Scenery.com
www.norwegian-scenery.com

Trade & Tourism Board of Portugal
www.portugal.org/tourism

Algarve - Life
www.algarve-life.com

Romanian Travel Guide
www.rotravel.com (Romania)

Russia Tourism
www.russia-tourism.com

All About Spain
www.red2000.com/spain

National Tourist Office of Spain
www.spaintour.com

Swedish Information Smorgasboard
www.sverigeturism.se/index-e.htm

Switzerland
www.lonelyplanet.com.au/dest/eur.swi.htm

Middle East

www.arab.net ArabNet			
Overall rating: ★ ★ ★ ★			
Classification: Information		**Readability:** ★ ★ ★ ★ ★	
Updating: Frequently		**Content:** ★ ★ ★ ★	
Navigation: ★ ★ ★ ★		**Speed:** ★ ★ ★ ★ ★	
JO			

This well-laid-out site is owned by a Saudi Research and Marketing Group, which also publishes Saudi's leading newspapers. It's the most comprehensive online resource on the Arab world, and it has a sense of humour as well: one of its directories is entitled the A–Z of Camels. It's not illustrated, however. The site covers the Middle East and parts of Africa, and has a section on each country, with information on history, culture and business. It also offers a tour guide. It is well worth a visit if you're planning a trip to the region, and makes good reading for the virtual traveller.

SPECIAL FEATURES

Arabview gives articles and opinions written in English by senior columnists and editors of Arab journals. All news topics are covered. The search facility is excellent, making this a priority site for business people and holidaymakers alike.

Middle East Internet Directory lists companies operating in the Middle East and Arab Africa. The companies are given alphabetically or by category. Retail and Trading is particularly relevant for the holidaymaker interested in shopping or the business traveller with a free afternoon.

Definitely worth a look for anyone going to the Middle East.

www.middle-east.com
MiddleEast

Overall rating: ★ ★ ★ ★			
Classification:	Information	**Readability:**	★ ★ ★ ★ ★
Updating:	Frequently	**Content:**	★ ★ ★ ★
Navigation:	★ ★ ★ ★	**Speed:**	★ ★ ★ ★

US

A great US-based site, full of information but currently specific to only Egypt, Lebanon, Syria and Jordan. It operates as an open-to-all global exchange site for business and leisure travellers to help plan trips and discover the Middle East.

Click on Countries to get to the links containing general information on the four featured countries, as well as the most well-known tourist destinations.

Each page is well illustrated, well written, and details the history and attractions of the town in question. Photographs are high quality and quick to download. Clicking on the Countries heading at the top of the page will take you back to the Countries menu.

SPECIAL FEATURES

Hotels lists hotels and prices by region. The good news is that apartments are also listed. The bad news is that in May 2000 the winter 1999–2000 prices were still listed.

Tours gives information from Anastasia Travel on one- to three-week tours in the four countries covered by the site. While all relevant information is given, online booking is not available.

Jobs helps enterprising individuals to find work in the Middle East, by allowing job hunters to post their resumés

and companies to advertise their vacancies. Registration is required to use this facility.

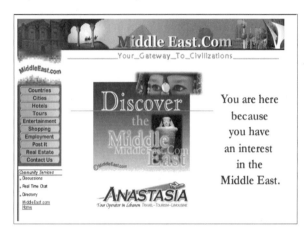

The site is definitely worth a visit, but since only mountain heights and population counts are given here under Culture, you'll need to go elsewhere for crucial travel tips such as not causing offence by taking off your clothes in the hotel gym changing room.

OTHER SITES OF INTEREST

Arabia.com
www.arabia.com

BruNet
www.brunet.bn

Tour Egypt
www.touregypt.net

Iran Online
www.iranonline.com

Israel Ministry of Tourism
www.goisrael.com

Lebanon On-Line Resources
www.lebanon-online.com

Syria Ministry of Tourism
www.syriatourism.org

Emirates.Org
www.emirates.org

Yemen Online
www.yemen-online.com

Jordan Tourism Board
www.tourism.com.jo

Chapter 2

online travel agents

'Knowledge may give weight, but accomplishments give lustre, and many more people see than weigh.'

Lord Chesterfield (1770)

Choosing or using an online agent or tour operator for the first time can be a daunting experience. What with the sheer size of the sites, the worry of giving credit card details over the Internet, and wondering if the holiday or tickets will be delivered, there's a lot to ponder.

Many online travel agents offer the same services, so deciding where to place your bets can be confusing. The large sites can be compared to supermarkets: each has huge amounts of stock, but lays it out in a different way. Using this analogy, you need go no further than examine your own food shopping preferences when deciding which online travel site to use.

Creatures of habit, who always visit the same supermarket and feel comfortable knowing where to find everything, will benefit from getting to know the layout of one particular site and then sticking with it. On the other hand, those who enjoy flitting here and there to small specialist shops will probably prefer to use the online travel boutiques, which can prove to be extremely rewarding.

Another potential worry when choosing online agents or tour operators is purchasing holidays or tickets over the internet. But set your mind at rest: an internet security system, Secure Sockets Layer (SSL), has been developed to protect against the possibility of credit card details falling into the wrong hands. Shopping on the net, if on a secure site, is now perfectly safe. Most browsers are able to determine whether or not sites are protected, and have some method for showing this, either a warning banner or an open or closed padlock icon at the bottom of the screen. In either case, get to know your browser's symbol for interpreting site security before proceeding.

A further and final worry can be the credibility of the company behind the website. It's all very well offering exotic holidays, but interested travellers want to feel confident that the holiday will be delivered. Just as with high street agents there are organisations and licenses that established agents belong to, which are very helpful in protecting the consumer. These agencies, such as The Association of British Travel Agents (ABTA), and Air Travel Organiser's Licence (ATOL), prevent customers from losing out should the company go bust. Check on each site to see if they are an accredited company, and then the best advice is just to use plain common sense.

Travel Agents

The agents are still fighting it out as to who will dominate on the web, but the following sites are the key players of the moment, and are the ones positioned to move forward as the dust settles. It's all a fairly new business in Britain and there are various tales of people booking rental cars and then turning up to find no record of the reservation, but by and large these stem from short-term teething problems and, in general, the online agents operate successfully.

www.a2btravel.com

a2btravel.com

Overall rating: ★ ★ ★ ★

Classification:	E-agent	Readability:	★ ★ ★ ★ ★
Updating:	Realtime	Content:	★ ★ ★ ★
Navigation:	★ ★ ★ ★ ★	Speed:	★ ★ ★ ★

UK

Offering all the services of a full-blown online agent, such as transportation, accommodation and information through linking to other well-known sites, a2btravel.com has a very pleasant European bias. The site, and all the links, are owned by the EMAP publishing group, who appear to have used their page layout know-how to construct very easy-to-read and use webpages.

The Villas in France and Eurostar and Ferries Timetable are large features of the homepage, and whilst the site offers worldwide possibilities, it is best suited for travellers with varying pocket depths, to, from and around the Continent.

SPECIAL FEATURES

Live Flight Arrivals presents live, up-to-the-minute flight arrival information direct from eight UK airports. A very handy page to mark for those who often have friends or family flying into the country.

UK Mapping gives very detailed online mapping for anywhere, urban or rural, in the UK.

Overall a very strong site for those interested in travelling around Europe. Although it caters to all at the moment, there may be a little more content for those looking for a bargain.

www.ebookers.com

Ebookers

Overall rating: ★ ★ ★ ★ ★

Classification:	E-agent	Readability:	★ ★ ★ ★
Updating:	Realtime	Content:	★ ★ ★ ★
Navigation:	★ ★ ★ ★ ★	Speed:	★ ★ ★ ★ ★

UK

Ebookers recently usurped both Expedia and Travelocity to become Europe's most popular online agent. It offers the same package of all travel-related services and booking capabilities. Again, this site is large but after a little while, one easily gets the hang of it and the speed is fast.

SPECIAL FEATURES

Services offers a list of services available to help the traveller in all aspects. It links to Travelcamel, which sells everything from sunscreen to mosquito nets. (Orders can be made online and products are delivered to the home.) It also links to a site for those on the move, offering a selection of communication websites for the traveller who needs to keep in touch with colleagues and friends, as well as a Travelclinic for medical queries.

Flight Watch is a feature currently offered only by ebookers, but it won't be long before the other agents catch on. Just enter the details of the flight you're tracking and ebookers will send a message of any change in its status to your mobile phone. No more sitting around wondering whether hubby will get to the restaurant on time! Flight Watch can be found under the Services channel.

Fare Alert lets ebookers be your watchdog 24 hours a day. As fares change daily, enter the fare you are willing to pay for a particular destination, and they will notify you if prices drop below this amount.

Around the World is the perfect page for those planning a gap-year. It offers round-the-world travel fares with varying routes, stop numbers and travel periods. Also on this page, hidden on the right-hand side, is a link to Tips On Around the World Flights, which is full of advice for the long-haul traveller.

World Guides links to www.Time.Out.com for excellent City information, and to www.LonelyPlanet.com for high quality overall destination information, including rural and remote areas. In addition, it offers a link to the great www.what'sonwhen.com, describing events all over the world.

This seems to be an advanced system online. Users will be very happy with the service.

www.edreams.com
eDreams

Overall rating: ★ ★ ★ ★			
Classification: E-agent		**Readability:**	★ ★ ★ ★ ★
Updating:	Realtime	**Content:**	★ ★ ★ ★ ★
Navigation:	★ ★ ★ ★	**Speed:**	★ ★ ★

UK

eDreams is a site that aims to provide a broad range of holidays suited to all tastes, as well as information and advice to help you plan your perfect holiday. It offers a selection of 'hand picked' holidays that can be browsed using the menu panel on the left of the screen by Activity (such as honeymoons or active journeys), or by Destination. Although the head office is in Barcelona, eDreams does have an office in London and is ABTA and IATA registered.

SPECIAL FEATURES

Special Offers such as cooking with Gary Rhodes in Grenada, Dream Holidays, such as a luxury golf holiday at the gorgeous Royal Westmoreland hotel in Barbados, and What's Hot, featuring such holidays as Ayurvedic Health holidays in Southern India, provide enticing examples of whats on offer.

Guides is what sets this site apart from other travel sites. It provides travel guides (called DreamGuides) who can answer questions and provide local information on a destination from finding you accommodation or restaurants, to providing suggestions on what to see and whether it is safe to travel to that place. Each guide also provides a list of links to websites that cover their area of expertise.

A great first stop, particularly if you want a holiday with a difference. The local 'DreamGuides' are a real bonus.

www.expedia.co.uk
Expedia

Overall rating: ★ ★ ★ ★ ★			
Classification:	E-agent	**Readability:**	★ ★ ★
Updating:	Realtime	**Content:**	★ ★ ★ ★
Navigation:	★ ★ ★ ★	**Speed:**	★ ★ ★

US

Owned by Microsoft, Expedia is one of the UK's oldest and largest travel-related sites, and is constantly updated and modified. It aims to give visitors the ability to find and book the right trip (including tickets, hotel rooms, car rentals, or full vacations) at the crucially important best price. Expedia offers more than 450 airlines, 40,000 hotels, all major car rental agencies, and more than 400 destination guides. The problem is definitely not the content, but the size of the site, which can seem overwhelming. However, most online agents share the same problem. As the site's getting on a bit compared with other sites, the low-key graphics also appear old-fashioned.

This site is not for anyone in a hurry, and is best suited to those with a specific task in mind, such as pricing a flight or seeking a hotel, rather than recreational browsing.

Expedia is a capable and reliable agent directed at the mainstream traveller looking for straightforward arrangements and competitive prices. It generally favours efficiency at the cost of imagery but in this case, that's a good thing.

The homepage is so full of titles, links and symbols that it can be difficult to find your way around. The best method is to start slowly from the top, jumping straight over the mumbo jumbo of section titles in white type, to the next line of plane, hotel, and car icons. This avoids the bombardment of unwanted advertising. If this fails, scroll down the homepage to the bottom and use Site Guide for an easily decipherable index to the site's different sections.

SPECIAL FEATURES

My Travel gives travellers the opportunity to register for personalised travel services which can store travel itineraries or track low fares to three frequently used destinations. It remembers personal details such as home airport and has a mileage minder, which keeps frequent travel information in one place. If you're going to use the site often, persevering with the one-off membership sign-in slog is definitely worth it.

Fare Compare shows fares other customers have found on a particular route, and suggests when to travel to obtain the most competitive fare. Only good for those with very flexible diaries.

Arrival/Departure Information should be bookmarked or added to your favorites if you are a frequent traveller. By using a drop-down menu of airlines, and then filling in a flight number or departure/destination information, it's possible to access up-to-the-minute information on arrivals and departures. The feature is currently only possible for about 20 airlines.

What's On When provides information about cultural, heritage, and family events taking place around the globe.

Overall, Expedia is one of the most popular online agents, as evidenced by the 'Too busy — should be able to serve you soon' page which pops up occasionally when booking.

www.travelocity.co.uk
Travelocity

Overall rating: ★ ★ ★ ★ ★			
Classification:	E-agent	**Readability:**	★ ★ ★
Updating:	Daily	**Content:**	★ ★ ★ ★
Navigation:	★ ★ ★ ★	**Speed:**	★ ★

US R

Using the SABRE reservation system (previously developed by American Airlines' technology arm), Travelocity.co.uk offers a full online agency capable of booking transportation and accommodation for UK customers. It also offers access to a vast database of destination and other travel-related information. The homepage is overcrowded, which is understandable given the amount of information available. The site can be slow to download, but a graphics-free option is available if you want more speed.

To book, online registration (a 30-second deal) is required. But for those visiting the site in the name of research, entering as a visitor is a twice-available option.

Bear in mind that dot-com and dot-co.uk access two different sites. The co.uk suffix will take you through to the UK site.

SPECIAL FEATURES

Best Fare which was previously available only on Travelocity's US site, is now available to its UK customers. The feature promises to come up with the very best fare available on a particular route; when checked, it came up with the same price as offline agents.

Weekend Deals presents the weary and overworked with some delightful ideas for getting away. Especially suitable for those who aren't used to splashing out.

Hotel Summary gives real pictures of the rooms, with extensive written details about the hotel and its location. To find Hotel Summary, enter Find/Reserve Hotel from the homepage, complete the hotel search fill-in-form and hey presto!

Seat Maps is to be found in the prime position at the very top of the homepage, and allows you to choose your favourite seat on a plane. This option is also offered when a flight on the participating airlines is booked. At the moment, only American Airlines and British Airways offer this facility but hopefully more airlines will soon follow suit.

Travel Tips presents a mixed bag of interesting and relevant information, including Best Fare Finder, Theatre Guide, Resort Guide, Baggage Guidelines and a Currency Converter.

Travel Tools on the other hand, found in the upper right-hand corner of the Homepage, allows visitors to register free, to benefit from the professional SABRE online booking facility as well. Once a member, visitors are allowed to check their own list of reservations with one click. This is also the page where you can check a ticket delivery status or change your registration details, such as address or telephone number.

Not much difference here between this and Expedia. Go with one and stick with it. Jumping ship will prove a waste of time.

www.travelselect.com
Travel Select

Overall rating: ★ ★ ★ ★ ★			
Classification:	E-agent	**Readability:**	★ ★ ★ ★ ★
Updating:	Realtime	**Content:**	★ ★ ★ ★ ★
Navigation:	★ ★ ★ ★ ★	**Speed:**	★ ★ ★ ★

UK

www.travelstore.com
travelstore.com

Overall rating: ★ ★ ★ ★ ★			
Classification:	E-agent	**Readability:**	★ ★ ★ ★ ★
Updating:	Regularly	**Content:**	★ ★ ★ ★
Navigation:	★ ★ ★ ★ ★	**Speed:**	★ ★ ★ ★ ★

US R

Brilliant! This fully online agent provides all travel services, and is graphically easy on the eye. Based in London, Travelselect was developed by Globepost Limited who, for years, have specialised in providing travel services to agents. Now they have expanded to include this online retail business.

In general, it offers flights, hotel accommodation and car rental worldwide, travel insurance and currency. It also offers a direct link to Eurostar's site for reservations and booking, but for other train journey information visits to another site are necessary. (see Chapter 3 - Train Travel).

SPECIAL FEATURES

Multi-Leg Itinerary is directed at those with other than standard-return journeys to research and book tickets.

City Guide links directly to Fodor's Travel Guide pages and you can, after choosing from a short checklist of required information such as lodging, restaurants or overview, create a personal mini guide. Visually this feature isn't the easiest to use as the site designers have chosen a split window presentation, which means a lot of unavoidable scrolling.

Although Travelselect appears to be directed at globe trotters, the immediately evident Eurostar feature on the homepage suggests they might be targeting a narrower audience.

This site is like a hunky football player, who also has a PhD. and runs a successful consulting firm as well. It has it all, is good-looking and on top of all that is nice.

In haste, at home or the office, you can buy air tickets, book hotels, hire a car, buy insurance, read the latest travel news, buy a travel guide, calculate currency changes, get travel points, print out itineraries and purchase records. The database includes 14,000 airports, 532 airlines, 40,000 hotels.

The homepage is top-tabbed with every service category. These are quickly reached and very simple to use. When looking for savings, make sure to choose 'bargain hunt' as your search by option.

You can access the site up to three times without registering. After this you must choose one of the registration options, both of which are free. Quick Registration entitles you to access the site up until the point of booking. Full Registration entitles you to unlimited access, 200 travel points and updates on travel news and special deals.

SPECIAL FEATURES

Travel Guides links you to short but complete summaries about destinations. These write-ups are jam-packed with activities and sightseeing opportunities to keep anybody busy for several days of touring, and to inform any business-tripper. They even include the radio frequencies for the BBC and the VOA.

Restaurant Guide is a powerful restaurant search that unexpectedly yielded some small, secret Parisian restaurants that are real treasures.

Corporate Accounts allows for expenses- and itinerary-tracking for a number of travelling employees.

Weather presents a five-day weather forecast for anywhere in the world; just choose the continent, the country and, finally, the city. At the bottom of the page, there's also a Convert into Fahrenheit feature for those who shy away from Celsius.

Travel Links offers a wide variety of choices for train services, ferry services, visa information, time zone checks, airport guides, travel health and advice as well as weather and currency information.

Whats on When links directly to the high-quality www.whatsonwhen.com.

A super-efficient and quality-packed travel store and travel management site.

www.travelweb.com
Travelweb

Overall rating: ★ ★ ★ ★ ★			
Classification:	E-agent	**Readability:**	★ ★ ★ ★
Updating:	Realtime	**Content:**	★ ★ ★ ★ ★
Navigation:	★ ★ ★ ★ ★	**Speed:**	★ ★ ★ ★

UK

Funky! For an online agent, TravelWeb has the hippest and most dotcom-style homepage to date. The graphics, which consist of childlike drawings and writing in chalk colours on a black background, don't exactly shout 'Take us very seriously, we are grown up and established', but navigating the site is child's play. The site offers two services: a link to Expedia (see p.41) for flight reservations, and its own page for hotel reservations.

SPECIAL FEATURES

Click-it! Weekends offers deals from participating hotel chains from around the world. Prices are published every Monday, and they promise to be the lowest of the low.

Overall, TravelWeb delivers what it promises, but one wonders whether there's really room for yet another site of this nature.

www.lastminute.com
Lastminute

Overall rating: ★ ★ ★ ★			
Classification:	E-agent	**Readability:**	★ ★ ★ ★
Updating:	Realtime	**Content:**	★ ★ ★ ★ ★
Navigation:	★ ★ ★ ★ ★	**Speed:**	★ ★ ★ ★

UK

Lastminute are on a mission: to encourage spontaneous, romantic, and sometimes adventurous behaviour by offering people the chance to live their dreams at unbeatable prices. Despite being designed in very fashionable colours and offering some interesting travel deals, this site suffers from a rather generic dotcom feel, and would benefit from having real travel-related experience behind it.

Lastminute has managed to negotiate some favourable rates with hotels and airlines, but the site's competitors now offer the same value-for-money trips. Still, its very nice to be greeted by such trendy colours, and some of the features are truly innovative. The quickest way to get to grips with what this site has to offer is to use the scroll-down site index on the left. This divides the site into various subsections such as What's Cool? and links to information for Today, Tomorrow, and Next Week.

SPECIAL FEATURES

Fully Booked helps visitors gain tickets, hotel rooms, or entry to the most wanted venues in the UK. Most don't appear to relate to travel, but the names of the establishments offering VIP cards through the site, such as Kinky Booty and Naughty But Nice, are good for a giggle.

A quirky site for flamboyant eccentrics with a flexible schedule.

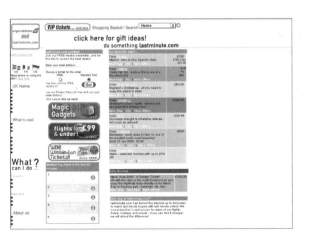

www.leisurehunt.com
LeisureHunt

Overall rating: ★ ★ ★ ★			
Classification:	EBooking	**Readability:**	★ ★ ★ ★ ★
Updating:	Regular	**Content:**	★ ★ ★ ★ ★
Navigation:	★ ★ ★ ★	**Speed:**	★ ★ ★ ★ ★

UK

This practical, straightforward, and speedy service offers a search by destination for hotels, bed and breakfasts, camp sites, hostels, and self catering. It's a wide-ranging, easily navigable site.

SPECIAL FEATURES

Speedbook is for real-time immediate booking of UK accommodation. It has a very good selection, good descriptions, and summaries of each entry.

A swift and wide-ranging accommodation booking service, most extensive in UK and larger foreign cities, but with vast worldwide listings suiting every budget and facility requirement.

www.utravel.co.uk
Utravel

Overall rating: ★ ★ ★ ★			
Classification:	E-agent	**Readability:**	★ ★ ★ ★ ★
Updating:	Regular	**Content:**	★ ★ ★ ★ ★
Navigation:	★ ★ ★ ★ ★	**Speed:**	★ ★ ★ ★

UK

Owned by United News and Media, this travel agent is geared towards the bargain end of the market. The predictably busy homepage lists special offers for departures within 24 hours, and destinations and flight information, as well as holiday brochures. A different set of headings on the left of the homepage link to currency, car hire, and hotel features.

SPECIAL FEATURES

Travel Secrets provides tips and explanations for travellers, for example a comparison of the cost of accommodation and meals in various destinations over the last two years, and advice on travelling to places of unrest.

Competitions is basically a source of free market research. To win free tickets to Madrid, for example, personal details must be submitted as well as answering a simple question about Madrid, which by the way, is contained in the text. Not for those looking for intellectual challenge, but more for those hanging their hopes on the very small odds of winning.

Brochures is very handy for gathering ideas, and links to holiday offers from a never-ending list of UK based tour operators. Click on a specific trip to read a brief explanation of each offer, and click again for a fuller description.

'U can change your life!' is the company motto, and there are plenty of opportunities to do so here.

OTHER SITES OF INTEREST

TravelWorld
www.travel.world.co.uk
The largest index of European travel agents and tour operators on the Internet. Having no American operators, it is mostly relevant for those in Europe or with an interest in Europe. No groovy pics, just the info! Very easy to navigate.

My Travel Guide
www.mytravelguide.com
Just as it says, this site is a guide to all aspects of travel, its online travel agency being only a small part. It offers flight, car, and accommodation booking, and is more for the

mainstream traveller than for those looking for five-star luxury hotels. To date, the flight booking capabilities appear to be stronger than the accommodation reservation feature.

World of Travel
www.worldoftravel.co.uk.
An Expedia copy but without the gusto - demonstrated by a

search for Athens, Greece, which turned up only one site, that of Olympic Airways, and a search for New Hampshire, USA, which brought up nothing relevant at all. Half of the homepage is taken up with recruitment adverts, and although the site is easy to read, it's uninspiring. It's not yet ready to compete in the big picture, but bear it in mind for the future.

World of Net
www.worldof.net/holiday

Thomas Cook
www.thomascook.co.uk

American Express Travel
http://travel.americanexpress.com

Can Be Done
www.canbedone.co.uk
A useful source of advice and specialist tours for travellers with disabilities.

Tour Operators

Who wants to sit surrounded by piles of paper and catalogues from different tour operators when comparing holidays and operators on the web can be this easy? Most of the following tour operators have developed easy-to-use sites, which provide some of the more fun surfing opportunities on the web.

www.clubmed.com
Club Med

Overall rating: ★ ★ ★			
Classification:	Brochure	**Readability:**	★ ★ ★ ☆
Updating:	Seasonal	**Content:**	★ ★ ★ ☆
Navigation:	★ ★ ★ ★ ★	**Speed:**	★ ★ ★ ★ ★

(FR)

An easy-to-use site with a fun style, in keeping with the Club Med village atmosphere. After choosing your home location, browse the site by entering either the Club Life, Village Directory, or Good Deals facilities, which give plenty of detail. Online booking isn't possible, but a telephone number is given. If you already have a Club Med village or location in mind, you can go direct from the bottom of the homepage.

SPECIAL FEATURES

Village Green is not a guide to environmentally friendly Club Med villages, but a list of chat rooms for GMs (Club Med's previous, current or prospective employees).

Today Discover offers a description of a selected village. One wonders if its purpose is to plug the less busy location?

A very easy-to-use site...well organised with, thankfully, no mention of the village dance.

www.elysianholidays.co.uk
Elysian Holidays

Overall rating: ★ ★ ★			
Classification:	Brochure	Readability:	★ ★ ★ ★
Updating:	Seasonal	Content:	★ ★ ★ ★
Navigation:	★ ★ ★ ★ ★	Speed:	★ ★ ★ ★ ★

UK

www.exodus.co.uk
Exodus

Overall rating: ★ ★ ★			
Classification:	Tour Operator	Readability:	★ ★ ★ ★ ★
Updating:	Regularly	Content:	★ ★ ★ ★ ★
Navigation:	★ ★ ★ ★	Speed:	★ ★ ★ ★ ★

UK

Elysian Holidays' site operates slightly differently from others: straight away you are asked to specify a holiday property preference. Categories include apartments, hotels, rustic houses, or villas. The site will then generate holiday suggestions. Alternatively, choose a holiday destination, from a choice of Greece, Spain and Portugal, The Caribbean, or Cyprus.

SPECIAL FEATURES

Candili gives details of fully inclusive creative activity holidays and special interest vacations that take place on the Candili Estate on the Greek Island of Evia. The estate, which originally belonged to the Noel-Baker family, has apparently been transformed into an idyllic retreat where yoga, traditonal Greek cookery, pottery, or playing the oboe, can be studied. Prices (excluding flights) and dates of courses are given.

Hotels and Yachts provides information on yacht charters from a number of destinations with a selection of vessels. Bare-boat charter is available, or crews and cooks can be organised.

A must for those with an interest in the Mediterranean or Caribbean. Booking is by email only.

This vast, easily manoeuvrable site gives a broad variety of holidays and great destination information, as well as those last-minute bargains you can't get in the brochures.

Exodus are a gold medal-winning tour operator and give concise and enticing summaries of their holidays, which are clearly organised on the homepage by type of adventure: Walking and Trekking, Biking Adventures, and Overland Expeditions. Almost everything interlinks with everything else, so the lack of a site map is not a problem. Online booking is not available, though it's simple enough to book by phone.

SPECIAL FEATURES

Late Getaways lists holidays which usually depart within a week to a month and are very reasonably priced. The site links to full details of each trip and to similar trips that can be booked further in advance.

Holiday Finder is useful to sort holiday options by date, region, type of activity, and price.

A world-class, adventurous site.

www.kuoni.co.uk
Kuoni

Overall rating: ★ ★ ★			
Classification:	Brochure	Readability:	★ ★ ★ ★
Updating:	Seasonal	Content:	★ ★ ★ ★
Navigation:	★ ★ ★ ★ ★	Speed:	★ ★ ★ ★ ★

UK R

This household-name site gives information on the thousands of holidays they offer in 55 exotic countries. Online booking is possible for some, but not all, of the destinations offered. For the other non-online booking locations, a telephone number is given. The site is well designed, making it easy for visitors to locate their subject of choice.

Registration offers any UK resident priority notification of special offers, late availability and promotions as soon as they become available. However, you don't have to be inundated with huge amounts of unwanted details; completing a questionnaire means that you will be sent only information that applies to you.

SPECIAL FEATURES

Weddings is located at the very bottom of the homepage, and features ideas on where and how to get married in a tropical paradise. The site explains that not only is this option different and interesting, but that it's also good value, being far more cost-efficient than a UK-based wedding. Options suggested vary from sunny beach weddings to flying over Las Vegas in a helicopter. Unfortunately, booking isn't possible online, but you can register for the weddings brochure or email for a personalised response.

The Travel Collection is another way of saying 'special offers', as this page provides a wide range of specially-created holidays throughout the world at exceptional value-for-money prices. There is a daily special offer but, again, booking is not possible online.

Specialist Travel links to a number of agents of Kuoni who differentiate themselves by offering specialist travel tours. A page gives a list of specialist groups, which include sport, music, travel for schools, travel for trade fairs and exhibitions as well as business, conference and incentive travel. The quantity of links and information for each interest group varies, but at the very least a telephone number is given, and usually there is much more.

Brochure Request allows you to request a brochure, which will be sent by snail mail, after you give your details over the net.

This site is a pleasure to use and leaves you feeling confident about any holiday booked with Kuoni.

www.markwarner.co.uk
Mark Warner

Overall rating: ★ ★ ★			
Classification:	Brochure	Readability:	★ ★ ★ ★ ★
Updating:	Seasonal	Content:	★ ★ ★ ★ ★
Navigation:	★ ★ ★ ★ ★	Speed:	★ ★ ★ ★

UK

A very user-friendly site. The Mark Warner Club holidays are broken down into catalogue divisions such as summer, ski, singles and couples, and late offers. Family holidays are a speciality. Use the simple menu bar at the top of the hompage to reach them.

The site is attractive, but is perhaps best used as an information source as the online booking facility is not one of the best. The company aim to contact the customer within two working days to discuss booking requests (others promise 24 hours). It's probably easier to phone at your own convenience.

SPECIAL FEATURES

Summer offers beach holidays, with plenty of watersports options, in 10 Mediterranean locations.

Late Offers displays a list of discounted holidays, but since they are at the expensive end of the market you'll have to go elsewhere for a real bargain.

Singles and Couples offers the chance to relax in a child-free environment.

Ski Choose from Skiing holidays in seven European locations.

An attractive online brochure with vacations for the young professional and families.

www.seasonsinstyle.com
Seasons in Style

Overall rating: ★ ★ ★			
Classification:	Tour Operator	Readability:	★ ★ ★
Updating:	Occasionally	Content:	★ ★ ★ ★
Navigation:	★ ★ ★ ★ ★	Speed:	★ ★ ★ ★ ★

UK R

This exquisite, easy-to-navigate site offers tailor-made holidays to a collection of the finest hotels in the world. It is an ABTA, IATA, and ATOL approved site with conservative graphics and a rather-too-small side bar. It's definitely not for those with shallow pockets.

SPECIAL FEATURES

Luxury Plus invites visitors to book a special offer holiday, which doesn't mean a discounted week, but rather a vacation with a twist. At the time of review, an offer invited holidaymakers to join Gary Rhodes, the TV chef and cookery writer, at the Calabash hotel in Grenada, to join in the filming of two evenings of cookery demonstrations.

If you like to travel in style and are prepared to pay the price, then this site is a must-see.

www.tropical.co.uk
Tropical Places

Overall rating: ★ ★ ★			
Classification:	Tour Operator	**Readability:**	★ ★ ★ ★ ★
Updating:	Monthly	**Content:**	★ ★ ★ ★
Navigation:	★ ★ ★ ★ ★	**Speed:**	★ ★ ★ ★

UK

This simple site, with some rather fuzzy seventies wallpaper, offers an online brochure for some of the most exotic holidays in the world, at affordable prices. Online booking is confirmed within 24 hours by telephone, making the site not necessarily the most technologically advanced, but nonetheless very efficient.

Drop-down menus give destinations for the four areas: The Caribbean, Africa and The Middle East, The Indian Ocean, and The Far East. There is a small page of information on each destination, and descriptions of seven-day tours.

Some reasonable holidays if you can compromise on flexibility. The site is FTO, ATOL, IATA, and ABTA approved.

www.travelspot.co.uk
Travelspot

Overall rating: ★ ★ ★			
Classification:	Tour Operator	**Readability:**	★ ★ ★ ★
Updating:	Frequently	**Content:**	★ ★ ★ ★
Navigation:	★ ★ ★ ★	**Speed:**	★ ★ ★

UK

Finally, a site with some mystery from this Chester-based retail travel agency. Place the cursor on one of eight blank white spots to enter Hot, Cool, Book, or one of the other categories. Even without the fun and games, this is an excellent site for hard-working people in need of a holiday. Shame that it doesn't offer online booking just yet.

SPECIAL FEATURES

Travelspots 2000 offers all-in packages to worldwide sporting events such as Grand Prix racing and rugby matches. The page gives some examples, but if you're interested, contact them by email for quotes.

If you choose your holiday by theme rather than destination then this site could be a useful starting point.

OTHER SITES OF INTEREST

Abercrombie and Kent
www.abercrombiekent.co.uk
A great site from the pioneers of luxury holidays to exotic and inaccessible places. Safaris are a speciality.

Elegant Resorts
www.elegantresorts.co.uk
This site is currently being revamped. It offers various seasonal luxury holidays, and is good if you're looking for the very top, very expensive hotels and resorts.

Elegant Resorts International
www.elegantresorts.com
Elegant Resorts originates from Elegant Resorts of Jamaica, and offers competitive packages for luxury accommodation in Jamaica, Haiti and Austria. Reservation requests are available online, but confirmation comes later by email or telephone.

Island Outpost
www.islandoutpost.com
A perfect site for those seeking boutique hotels in Miami, Jamaica or the Bahamas.

Concierge
www.concierge.com
Owned by Condé Nast through CondéNet, Concierge links to Expedia (see p.41), Fodor's (see p.43), and Condé Nast Traveler magazine (see p.143). Although it has a strong US bias, it's a must for hedonists looking for a little exotic luxury, as it lists top spas and resorts worldwide. It's not always possible to book on site.

Page and Moy
www.pageandmoy.co.uk
At the time of review, you could only order brochures online but this is an attractive offering from respected purveyors of specialist tours including motor racing, arts, gardens, opera and music tours.

Powder Byrne
www.powderbyrne.co.uk
This slick, easy-to-use, site offers information on PowderByrne's up-market ski and sun holidays for families. There is also an interesting section for corporate groups. Enquiries can be made by email although, like most tour operators, bookings cannot be made online. The intention is that the site will also offer a ski portal, with the best ski information on the web including ski maps, weather, snow quality reports and local information, in the near future.

Scott Dunn
www.scottdunn.com
The Scott Dunn website has been under construction for most of 2000, but hopefully by the Autumn it will be up and running, providing a wealth of information on their worldwide sun and ski holidays. For notification of the site's launch enter the site and fill in your email address.

British Airways
www.british-airways.com/holiday (See p. 60)

Virgin Holidays
www.virginholidays.co.uk

Disney
www.disney.com (See p. 96)

Orient-Express Tours
www.orient-expresstrains.com

Travel Service Auctioneers

The Auctioneers started life on the web as the most popular type of travel site, but with the increase in agent and operator sites their popularity has decreased. This doesn't mean they are not effective. People, usually those with flexible schedules, can scoop up some fantastic deals on the following sites.

www.qxl.com
QXL

Overall rating: ★ ★ ★

Classification:	Auction House	**Readability:**	★ ★ ★ ★ ★
Updating:	Daily	**Content:**	★ ★ ★ ★ ★
Navigation:	★ ★ ★ ★ ★	**Speed:**	★ ★ ★ ★

UK R

This pan-European auction site offers consumer-to-consumer and business-to-consumer auctions across eight European countries. It works by making deals with companies for their slow-moving stock. Auctions for flight tickets on this site usually last for 24 hours, and after logging a bid (a twenty second deal) you wait and watch as other bids come in on the page. If a bid is successful, QXL and the seller will email at the close of auction to confirm details. You can also opt to be emailed if you've been outbid in an ongoing auction, giving you the opportunity to re-enter the race.

The site's strength is in obtaining business class flight seats at absurdly low prices, although the Travel Accessories page is still rather weak, offering as it does only a long list of aqua shoes, a few flasks, and other odd bits. Presumably this will pick up over time.

To get to the travel-related items, click on The Travel Shop on the home page. Select from an index of categories such as Activity Holidays, Car Holidays, Family Holidays, and Villas and Cottages. It's not too overwhelming, and most definitely one of the more tolerable sites, given its size.

SPECIAL FEATURES

I am new to QXL walks you through the process of bidding online and explains how to find your desired items on the site. Within this section you'll find the Bidder's Guide, which explains how to place bids, how a bid limit works and how the auction functions. It also clarifies the buying process and what happens when you make a successful bid. About Bidding covers an extensive list of topics, such as: covering yourself against fraud, making a bid, and how much to bid.

Worth a visit for the clear explanations of the auction process, even if you can't find anything worth bidding for.

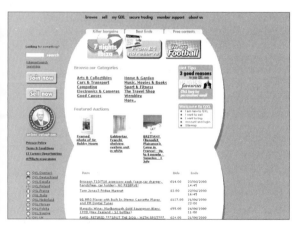

OTHER SITES OF INTEREST

Last Minute.com
www.lastminute.com
(see p. 45) For holidays, flights, and hotels.

Fired Up
www.firedup.com
For holidays, flights, and unusual holidays, as well as tickets to events such as Grand Prix racing.

Ebay
www.ebay.co.uk
Offers the usual, but bidders must have a very keen eye to find the travel category. (Click on Other Categories and scroll down.)

Chapter 3

direct booking online

'If it were done when tis done, then if twere well It were done quickly'

William Shakespeare 1564-1616, Macbeth (1606)

Sometimes you don't need all the services of the mammoth online travel agencies, and are better served by linking direct to the airline, hotel, or other service provider. In the future, this route should become much more price-friendly, as the companies behind them cut out agents' commissions and offer faster and faster service. Currently, though, it's still a chaotic market, with consumers sometimes getting the best price online and sometimes not. However, there's nothing more satisfying than having all the information at your fingertips!

Air Travel

The following airlines on the web offer useful sites for the British traveller. Do beware of the prices quoted, however, as until the dust settles on the amounts airlines are going to pay out to agents, prices vary greatly. Travellers might still benefit from shopping around, but the sites have many further uses beyond booking tickets.

http://flyaow.com
Airlines of the Web

Overall rating: ★ ★ ★ ★ ★			
Classification:	Links	**Readability:**	★ ★ ★ ★
Updating:	Realtime	**Content:**	★ ★ ★ ★
Navigation:	★ ★ ★ ★	**Speed:**	★ ★ ★ ★ ★

US R

AOW was created by a university professor and a handful of travel companies, and is best used as an index and link to worldwide airlines and their official websites. It also offers agency capabilities such as car and accommodation bookings, as well as cyber fares and air travel tips. It's the perfect site for those who need to check specific flight details and don't want to get caught up in an over-large and overwhelming online agent.

Although there is a rather official-looking log-in section on the left of the homepage, everything is available to the first time visitor as a guest.

SPECIAL FEATURES

Private Plane Charter links directly to www.AirCharter.com to allow visitors (or fantasisers alike) to research executive and group air charters. Registration is necessary to book.

Adventure is for those who would like to plan a special interest holiday. Linking to www.away.com it offers information on every kind of holiday imaginable, from nature packages to educational trips.

This is the best site for flight-related queries such as whether or not that new bicycle collected on your holiday will count as excess baggage!

www.britishmidland.co.uk
British Midland

Overall rating: ★ ★ ★ ★			
Classification:	Airline	Readability:	★ ★ ★ ★ ★
Updating:	Realtime	Content:	★ ★ ★ ★
Navigation:	★ ★ ★ ★ ★	Speed:	★ ★ ★ ★ ★

UK

British Midland's well-laid-out and straightforward site offers information and booking capability for flights on the busiest and most competitive routes in Europe. The airline has recently initiated a co-ordination venture with Lufthansa and Scandinavian Airlines, making the site well worth visiting for the European traveller.

Very occasionally the homepage's black background makes it a little hard on the eyes, but this doesn't affect the site's overall quality and efficiency.

SPECIAL FEATURES

Special Offers can be found under two different click-here invitations on the homepage, both linking to the same information. The offers are limited to travel from Heathrow and to a two-night minimum stay, including a Saturday. The maximum stay is for one month. Unlike some discount sites, there is a larger window for booking as the prices on offer are available for purchase for up to three months.

News presents updates on British Midland's constant partnership expansion initiatives and sponsorship agreements. Check here to see if your most frequent route is going to become part of British Midland's timetable.

Diamond Club gives a compelling argument for joining British Midland's frequent flier programme. It's easy to join online and, once a member, this page will soon allow for membership and destination point checks. Diamond club can be found on the site's menu at the bottom of the homepage.

Leisure gives information on how economy class travellers can get the best value for money. It also offers information on the Europe Air Pass, which is priced according to mileage band, but is available only for travellers coming from outside Europe. Group Reservations and planning arrangements for ten or more people travelling together can also be found under this Leisure heading.

Timetable asks you to choose your departure airport and destination airport from dropdown menus, and will then present a concise timetable of available flights. It's very simple and easy to use, and avoids endless scrolling, which some larger timetables encourage.

A brilliant, easy-to-use site for the European traveller. It might be useful for some other websites to take note of why the British Midland site is so successful.

www.virgin-atlantic.com
Virgin Atlantic

Overall rating: ★ ★ ★ ★			
Classification:	Airline	**Readability:**	★ ★ ★ ★ ★
Updating:	Realtime	**Content:**	★ ★ ★ ★ ★
Navigation:	★ ★ ★ ★	**Speed:**	★ ★ ★ ★ ★

UK R

Trust Richard Branson to get it right! Virgin Atlantic's website is easy to read, navigate and use. The homepage offers six categories of information, but the bright red screen can take its toll, so have some shades ready.

The homepage is a picture of part of a Virgin plane with some windows. The lower three windows have moving images, which are sometimes difficult to access. If these icons don't produce anything, all the information is available through the other links.

SPECIAL FEATURES

Join In is an odd name for a category that includes special offers, destination, weather and currency information. The only nuisance is the logging-in requirement, but endure the torture as the site is linked to other quality sites and it's worth the bother.

Book Now offers online booking, schedules, all flight information and special offers.

Where and When gives the route network, flight schedules, a description of the fleet and airline alliances. And just in case your retail therapy is likely to get out of hand, baggage allowance details are provided.

Aircraft Names is hidden away as a page in its own right under Our Fleet, and presents a list of Virgin's aircraft names, which makes for amusing reading, if nothing else.

Our Services offers Travel Classes, which isn't about lessons on how to travel, but rather a description of Virgin's Upper, Premium Economy, Economy and Business classes. This category also gives a list of films, television, audio and game programmes offered on each flight under Entertainment.

Tax Free Shopping is to be found under the above-mentioned Our Services category, and is the Virgin Atlantic Retail Therapy 2000 initiative. For this, you must register on the Join-In page, after which you can pre-order duty-free goods by fax or phone, to collect once on board a Virgin flight. There is a much larger range available here than on board, and product allowances differ according to where you are flying. This feature is only available to UK residents.

Virgin is the 2000 winner of the best airline - Atlantic business class and its site is one of the grooviest airline sites on the web by far, even though some of the category titles can be slightly confusing.

www.britishairways.com
British Airways

Overall rating: ★ ★ ★		
Classification: Airline	Readability:	★ ★ ★ ★
Updating: Realtime	Content:	★ ★ ★ ★
Navigation: ★ ★ ★	Speed:	★

UK

BA's UK homepage is something of a disappointment. Although worldwide timetables are available for up to a year in advance, online booking is not yet offered at competitive prices. Information on BA package holidays is available, but only if one is willing to hang around and wait. Speed is not of the essence on this site. Ignore the plea for registration, as it merely allows use of the My Travel feature which tracks flights and mileage.

SPECIAL FEATURES

Eticket allows late boarding and last minute itinerary changes. Electronic tickets mean no paper and the opportunity to book up to 30 minutes before check-in time. British Airways' computers will store all your information and you simply present yourself at the check-in desk, or for the traveller with hand baggage, go directly to the self-service check-in machine. This feature is only available online to members of the frequent flier mileage program, the Executive Club.

Seat Planner shows site visitors the layout of the fleet aircrafts. As timetables give the planned aircraft type, it's possible to avoid being fobbed off at check-in by an over-zealous airline employee, and prove that your good seat assignment is actually next to or behind the toilets.

Probably of most use to existing BA customers.

OTHER SITES OF INTEREST

Airlines of the Web
http://flyaow.com/frequentflyer.
This page of the AOW site (see p.58) offers a fairly comprehensive alphabetical scroll-down menu of links to all airlines and air mile official sites. Well worth a click or two for those whose New Year resolution was to get to grips with tracking multiple frequent flyer program memberships.

Airmiles — Travel the World
www.airmiles.co.uk
Just as with any club query, you must have the membership number to get anywhere. Oh, and don't forget your password too. Once you've hurdled these obstacles this website is great for account information and booking inquiries.

Aer Lingus
www.aerlingus.ie

Aeroflot
www.aeroflot.co.uk

Air Canada
www.aircanada.ca

Air France
www.airfrance.co.uk

Air India
www.allindia.com/airindia

Alitalia
www.italiatour.com

All Nippon Airways
http://src.ana.co.jp/eng/index.html

American Airlines
www.americanair.com

Ansett Airlines
www.ansett.com.au

Cathay Pacific
www.cathaypacific-air.com

Delta Airlines
www.delta-air.com

Easyjet
www.easyjet.com

Emirates Airlines
www.emirates.com
IRS winner of overall best airline 2000
OAG Airline of the year 1999

Finnair
www.finnair.co.uk

Go
www.go-fly.co.uk

Iberia
www.iberia.com/ingles/home.html

Icelandair
www.icelandair.co.uk

Japan Airlines
www.jal.co.jp/english/index_e.html

KLM
www.klmuk.com

Lufthansa
www.lufthansa.com

Malaysia Airlines
www.malaysiaairlines.com.my

Qantas
www.qantas.com.au
IRS winner of best airline - world first class 2000

Ryanair
www.ryanair.com

Sabena
www.sabena.com

SAS
www.sas.se

Singapore Airlines
www.singaporeair.com

Swissair
www.swissair.com
IRS winner of best airline - European business class 2000

Thai Airways International
www.thaiair.com

TWA
www.twa.com

United Airlines
www.ual.com

Road Travel

www.avis.co.uk
Avis

Overall rating: ★ ★ ★ ★ ★			
Classification:	Car Rental	**Readability:**	★ ★ ★ ★ ★
Updating:	Realtime	**Content:**	★ ★ ★ ★ ★
Navigation:	★ ★ ★ ★ ★	**Speed:**	★ ★ ★ ★ ★

US

A fairly comprehensive site, where a combination of pull-down menus and fill-in-the-blanks allows quotes and booking for any category of car from its many rental stations. Its particular geographical strength is the US, but it has a strong global presence.

The real find with Avis's site is the ability to book online rentals where pick-up is at one location and drop-off is at another. Many rental car sites don't yet offer this.

SPECIAL FEATURES

Special Offers advertises rental cars for £13 per day for American Express cardholders, as well as a chance to win a new sports car.

UK Renting Guide is aimed at tourists travelling to Britain, as opposed to UK residents.

Avis Products describes Avis Advance, which offers benefits to small businesses, such as how to get a mobile phone for use in the UK or abroad, or how to rent prestige cars through Avis online.

An easy-to-use, and not too overwhelming, car rental site.

www.hertz.co.uk
Car Rental

Overall rating: ★ ★ ★ ★ ★			
Classification:	Airline	**Readability:**	★ ★ ★ ★
Updating:	Realtime	**Content:**	★ ★ ★ ★
Navigation:	★ ★ ★ ★ ★	**Speed:**	★ ★ ★

US

This is a well-laid-out, easy-to-use site in corporate colours. It is directed mostly at those that intend to join the Small Business Program. The prices for individuals are not always the most competitive. Shame about the speed.

The best navigation tip is to go first to Worldwide Locations to get the code for picking up car locations, which avoids a three-step process later.

SPECIAL FEATURES

Special Offers doesn't mean that one is offered a discounted rental car and then expected to travel to the Sahara to take it up, but gives details of vouchers that are on offer next time a Hertz car is booked. Vouchers usually comprise discount accommodation or admission to various tourist attractions.

A good site for business users, though individuals may find more competitive prices elsewhere.

www.rentadeal.com

Rentadeal

Overall rating: ★ ★ ★ ★			
Classification:	Search Engine	**Readability:**	★ ★ ★ ★
Updating:	Realtime	**Content:**	★ ★ ★ ★
Navigation:	★ ★ ★ ★ ★	**Speed:**	★ ★ ★

US

For those travellers visiting major European or US cities, this rent-a-car search engine with online car reservation capabilities is a dream. It will get quotes and availability information on up to 13 rental car companies, which saves visiting 13 different websites. The site also claims that visitors can save 30 per cent on rental car prices. The only drawback is that all quotes are given in US dollars and there isn't an on-site currency converter.

Use the drop-down destination menu or scroll down the homepage and click to find the desired location. Answer a few questions about required timings and car standards, and the site does the rest.

SPECIAL FEATURES

Other Cities is hidden away at the bottom of the International Cities drop-down menu, and allows searches for many more cities than specified. Don't be put off by the small number of cities shown on the homepage.

A site especially suited to those needing a rental car in Europe or the United States, and who are addicted to comparing prices.

OTHER SITES OF INTEREST

London Travel Information
www.londontransport.co.uk
Information for those who need to get around London by bus, underground, or using river services. Look out for the interactive journey planner which should be available soon.

GobyCoach.com
www.nationalexpress.co.uk
Wherever you are travelling this site offers online travel information on fares, timetables, and alternatives fot the UK and Europe. Of particular interest is the Shuttle Services feature which gives the fares and timetables of services to all UK airports.

Holiday Autos
www.holidayautos.com

Budget
www.drivebudget.com

Street Eagle Harley Rentals
www.streeteagle.com
For Harley Davidson rentals in the United States only.

RAC Route Planner
www.rac.co.uk (see p. 120)

EasyRentacar
www.easyRentacar.com

Alamo
www.alamo.com

Rail Travel

The train companies appear to be more forward in their web technology than they do in their core business of railroad transport. Most of the official sites are easy to use and beat waiting on the end of a phone line for information. The sites generally offer schedules, train status check facilities and some online ticket purchasing.

United Kingdom

www.gner.co.uk
GNER

Overall rating: ★ ★ ★ ★			
Classification:	Search Engine	**Readability:**	★ ★ ★ ★ ★
Updating:	Realtime	**Content:**	★ ★ ★ ★
Navigation:	★ ★ ★ ★ ★	**Speed:**	★ ★ ★ ★ ★

UK

Owned by Sea Containers, GNER operates trains from London Kings Cross to Northern Scotland, with many stops along the way. Its innovative website offers online reservation and ticket purchasing.

SPECIAL FEATURES

How's My Train Running enables visitors to check GNER train arrivals and departures. Running on real time, this train status check facility is one of the most advanced of UK websites.

Route Info is a slight misnomer, since it contains tourist's titbits for the towns en route, rather than route planning information.

Timetable allows you to plan your departure time and travel route to your selected destination.

Questions lists the most commonly asked customer service questions and provides you with a range of answers.

Tickets explains the different types of ticket available and how to book.

A one-stop shop, for anyone taking the train to the North of England.

www.thetrainline.com
Thetrainline

Overall rating: ★ ★ ★ ★			
Classification:	Ticket Agent	**Readability:**	★ ★ ★ ★ ★
Updating:	Realtime	**Content:**	★ ★ ★ ★
Navigation:	★ ★ ★ ★ ★	**Speed:**	★ ★ ★ ★ ★

UK R

This is the site for the UK rail traveller, although don't forget the importance of the article in the address. www.trainline.com is not what you are looking for if you are interested in railroad travel, as it is a promotional site for a rock band. Thetrainline gives train times, ticket bookings, and seat reservations for any train operator in mainland UK. Shame about the irritating registration required for the first time user.

SPECIAL FEATURES

National Conditions is a clear and easily legible list of all the national terms and conditions relating to train travel. Well worth a visit for unusual situations like ticket loss or changes of plan.

A useful site for planning your UK travel, though for best fares you may be better going straight to individual rail companies.

www.railtrack.co.uk
Railtrack

Overall rating: ★ ★			
Classification:	Information	**Readability:**	★ ★ ★
Updating:	Frequently	**Content:**	★ ★ ★ ★
Navigation:	★ ★ ★	**Speed:**	★ ★ ★

UK

Although this site doesn't offer online booking capabilities or links, it makes a nice little passenger resource for UK train travellers. There is a searchable timetable providing times and availability for offered routes as well as a travel news section, which presents articles on topics that could effect your commute in the future. Beyond those features, this site is best suited to the city investor looking for company information.

Most useful to those seeking business information, but with some decent tidbits for commuters and travellers.

OTHER SITES OF INTEREST

Midland Main Line
www.mml.rail.co.uk

ScotRail
www.scotrail.co.uk

South West Trains
www.swtrains.co.uk

Thames Trains
www.thamestrains.co.uk

Virgin Trains
www.virgintrains.co.uk

Europe

www.eurostar.com
Eurostar

Overall rating: ★ ★ ★ ★			
Classification: Information		**Readability:**	★ ★ ★ ★ ★
Updating: Realtime		**Content:**	★ ★ ★ ★ ★
Navigation: ★ ★ ★ ★ ★		**Speed:**	★ ★ ★ ★ ★

UK R

Eurostar offers a speedy, efficient, and straightforward website to match its service, which runs to Paris, Lille, Brussels, Disneyland, and the French Alps. Timetables and booking pages are easy to get to from a very clear homepage, but no price discount is offered for booking online.

SPECIAL FEATURES

Frequent Traveller gives benefits to those who travel often between Waterloo and Paris. Its possible to enrol online and then reap the benefits of express check-in, late check-out at partner hotels, and points toward free Eurostar tickets.

Ski Train gives travellers the option of two trains direct to the Alps with automatic connections to major ski resorts such as Val D'Isere, Tigne, and Meribel. Passengers are allowed one set of skis, boots, and poles free of charge. To find your way to Ski Train, enter Destination and click on Alps. For some reason this service does not come up on the timetable page.

An impeccable online offering from Eurostar.

<table>
<tr><td colspan="4">www.raileurope.co.uk
Rail Europe</td></tr>
</table>

www.raileurope.co.uk			
Rail Europe			
Overall rating: ★ ★ ★ ★			
Classification: Information		**Readability:**	★ ★ ★ ★ ★
Updating: Realtime		**Content:**	★ ★ ★ ★
Navigation: ★ ★ ★ ★ ★		**Speed:**	★ ★ ★ ★ ★
FR R			

Rail Europe is the largest distributor of European travel-related products, catering for both the leisure and business traveller. Known best for their famous Eurailpass for travel on Continental Europe, they now offer a complete line of BritRail passes plus point-to-point tickets on any route in Europe and even Russia.

It doesn't stop at the rail-related products either. They also cover hotel and car rental as well as transatlantic air tickets. Overall they cover services for 35 countries.

A rewarding site for any UK or continental rail traveller.

OTHER SITES OF INTEREST

Eurotunnel
www.eurotunnel.com

Rail Connection
www.railconnection.com

United States

www.4trains.com			
4Trains			
Overall rating: ★ ★ ★ ★			
Classification: Reservations		**Readability:**	★ ★ ★ ★ ★
Updating: Realtime		**Content:**	★ ★ ★ ★
Navigation: ★ ★ ★ ★ ★		**Speed:**	★ ★ ★ ★ ★
US			

As part of the 4Anything search engine, this site is best suited for those looking for train services in North America, in particular the US, although Europe does gets a small mention. The site operates in the typical search format, with various self-explanatory categories given on the homepage. In addition to all the rail categories offered, this site has many links to its generic search engine.

SPECIAL FEATURES

Organizations & Agencies is the page for train enthusiasts. It offers links to many train-related associations and societies.

Attractions & Museums is another page for those interested in trains, or for parents in North America looking for child-friendly activities. It offers links to the Grand Canyon Railway, The Great American Train Show and other similar entities.

Publications allows visitors to read up on the latest information about railroads, with links to train magazines and model railroad publications.

Overall, a great site for those travelling by rail in North America and train enthusiasts alike. (see also Amtrak at www.amtrak.com.)

Worldwide

www.travelnotes.org
Travelnotes

Overall rating: ★ ★ ★ ★			
Classification: Reservations		**Readability:**	★ ★ ★ ★ ★
Updating: Realtime		**Content:**	★ ★ ★
Navigation: ★ ★ ★ ★ ★		**Speed:**	★ ★ ★ ★ ★

US

Part of the extensive www.travelnotes.org, this site operates as a search engine providing links to hundreds of train sites, to help you get the most out of rail travel, from choosing passes and discovering more about different countries to getting information on train times.

SPECIAL FEATURES

Destinations is found on the left-hand side of the page, and offers links to masses of good quality destination information around the world.

Random Link presents a mystery tour of Travelnotes pre-selected travel websites. Found at the very bottom of the Destinations menu, it can be a lot of fun for those with extra time on their hands.

Most definitely the best site for finding official train and railroad sites around the world.

www.travelsource.com/trains.html
Travel Source

Overall rating: ★ ★ ★ ★ ★			
Classification: Directory		**Readability:**	★ ★ ★ ★ ★
Updating: Frequently		**Content:**	★ ★ ★ ★
Navigation: ★ ★ ★ ★ ★		**Speed:**	★ ★ ★ ★ ★

US

This is one of the most comprehensive online lists of worldwide train and railroad websites.

To find information on rail travel, you must have a region in mind. Use the alphabetical drop-down menu for international destinations or, easier still, use the Go Locations search page to find railroad sites in exotic locations.

OTHER SITES OF INTEREST

Voyages Jules Verne
www.vjv.co.uk

Trans-Siberian Express
www.trans-siberian.co.uk

Australia's Great Train Journeys
www.gsr.com.au

Orient-Express Trains and Cruises
www.orient-expresstrains.com

Sea Travel

Another joy of our worldwide web. Now if travelling to a Greek Island for a holiday, we can find the times and information abut the ferry schedules from the mainland online. The following sites can provide information on ferries and ships worldwide. One can even reserve online and receive the tickets by snail mail for European ferry travel.

www.cruise.com
Cruise.com

Overall rating: ★ ★ ★ ★			
Classification:	Information	**Readability:**	★ ★ ★ ★ ★
Updating:	Frequently	**Content:**	★ ★ ★ ★
Navigation:	★ ★ ★ ★ ★	**Speed:**	★ ★ ★ ★ ★

US

A huge site that caters to the very popular US cruise market. Booking is by telephone, and discounts are offered. This is an interesting site for those wishing to sail from a US port. It also caters to the cruising enthusiast, offering all sorts of cruise information, including Cruise Tips, Cruise Books as well as Dining Menus.

SPECIAL FEATURES

Special Cruises divides all the cruises the site has on offer into special interest categories. Instead of searching the whole site for cruises for kids or kosher cruises, you can find the links here.

Travel Links provides access to related sites, such as accessories, cruise lines, currency, tour deals and travel suppliers. This might be useful for UK residents wishing to find a comprehensive list of cruise liners without using an extensive and cumbersome generic search engine.

A well-organised and easy-to-use site.

www.cruise2.com
Cruise2

Overall rating: ★ ★ ★ ★			
Classification:	Information	**Readability:**	★ ★ ★
Updating:	Frequently	**Content:**	★ ★ ★ ★
Navigation:	★ ★ ★ ★ ★	**Speed:**	★ ★ ★

US

A huge non-profit website, this is the largest cruise portal on the web, with every imaginable additional feature. It links to what seems like every cruise line or agent in existence, or you can check out Surf the Cruise News, Cabin Exchange or Safety at Sea. The gateway page is certainly different, with its elaborately scrawled pink writing announcing the Shipping Center, but it is not particularly easy on the eye. The same goes for the homepage and its illustrations.

This site serves travellers, agents and cruise lines, with links catering to all three. For a portal, this site is excellent offering a lot of high-quality information.

SPECIAL FEATURES

Cruise Finder offers an enormous database, which can be searched in several ways: sail date, destination, cruise line, ship departure point or cost.

This site is an excellent, comprehensive index to all possible links relating to the world of shipping and cruising.

www.ferrytravel.de
Ferry Companies of the World

Overall rating: ★ ★ ★ ★			
Classification:	Directory	**Readability:**	★ ★ ★ ★ ★
Updating:	Quarterly	**Content:**	★ ★ ★ ★
Navigation:	★ ★ ★ ★ ★	**Speed:**	★ ★ ★ ★ ★

G

A beautifully designed site with delightful sound effects (a ship's horn bellows as one enters the homepage), which demonstrates with great panache the glory and usefulness of the web. A directory gives links to the official websites of ferry companies across the globe, and quarterly updates are offered. The site serves everyone from the Dover to Calais day-tripper to the more exotic Greek island-hopper or Asian water-cruiser.

Navigation couldn't be easier. The homepage presents a list of eight regions of the world, and from there you are presented with a list of ferry companies of the area. Most regions offer quite lengthy lists, with South America being the shortest, but this indicates Latin America's state of doing business on the web versus any failure of the site itself.

Oddly, there is no About Us section, so you can't be sure of the origins of the site. One can, however, conclude from the 'de' at the end of the URL that it is a German enterprise.

A definite must for a ferry-seeker.

OTHER SITES OF INTEREST

Cunard Line
www.cunardline.com
An attractive homepage beckons would-be cruisers aboard classic ocean cruises. You can read about the history of Cunard Cruising, as well as view their destination list and itineraries.

CruiseOpinion.com
www.cruiseopinion.com
Database site containing 3500 cruise reviews, submitted by cruise veterans. Useful resource if you want honest reviews straight from the horse's mouth.

TravelPage.com
www.travelpage.com/cruise
Extensive list of ship profiles, cruise reviews and latest news. There's also a section called Cruise Talk where you can discuss every aspect of cruising with fellow enthusiasts, if you really want to...

Youra.com e.guides
www.youra.com/ferry
Guide to local and international ferry services for a selected number of countries. Good for route-planning in countries where the waterways form an integral part of the public transport system.

Royal Caribbean International
www.royalcaribbean.com

P&O Cruises
www.pocruises.com

Princess Cruises and Tours
www.princesscruises.com

Freesun
www.freesun.be/cruises.html

Accommodation

When booking a holiday or a business trip the sites listed on the next pages will help ensure that your accommodation offers everything that you might want. No more ending up in a hotel with 832 rooms when you were really looking for something small and intimate, or turning up with Fido at your heel when no pets are allowed.

www.1001-villa-holidaylets.com

1001 Villas

Overall rating: ★ ★ ★ ★ ★			
Classification:	Index	**Readability:**	★ ★ ★ ★
Updating:	Frequently	**Content:**	★ ★ ★ ★
Navigation:	★ ★ ★ ★ ★	**Speed:**	★ ★ ★ ★ ★

UK

It is immediately obvious that this site has a lot to offer. The homepage is very, very crowded, but with a little patience it soon becomes obvious what to do. A search can be made for properties either by Country or Rental Property Name, using scroll-down menus, or there is a Quick Search index on the left side of the homepage featuring topics such as Top Golf, World Regions, and Sport Search. Properties are rented directly from the owners.

SPECIAL FEATURES

Hot Property gives the details of one of the best properties the site has to offer, such as a newly restored 200-year-old Spanish farmhouse renting in the prime summer months for £1200 per week.

Latest Properties is a nice feature which allows visitors to feel that they are getting the first look at the new stock on the books, and not being left with the discarded remainders.

The site offers a lot all over the world, although the photos can sometimes be difficult to view, a problem it shares with other sites.

www.theaa.co.uk/hotels/

AA Hotel Guide

Overall rating: ★ ★ ★ ★ ★			
Classification:	Guide	**Readability:**	★ ★ ★ ★
Updating:	Annually	**Content:**	★ ★ ★ ★
Navigation:	★ ★ ★	**Speed:**	★ ★ ★ ★

UK

A very easy-to-use guide to regional UK hotels, which forms just part of the AA Guide to Britain. It can be searched by brand or consortium as well as location. There's no online booking, but the site is very informative about places to stay, even in the remotest parts of the UK.

The AA can be forgiven for the rather uninspiring design of the homepage, since what it lacks in aesthetic appeal it more than makes up in the amount and quality of information on offer.

From the homepage, select the destination by either clicking on the map of the UK or the list of areas that appears down the left-hand side of the page. To select Groups and Consortia scroll down to the links at the bottom of the page. Once in the desired region, you can select your accommodation type, level of quality and price band. The list is comprehensive and includes accommodation ranging from modest inns to five-star hotels.

There's also a list of places to eat, which, though extensive, pays little or no attention to anything other than English or French cuisine.

SPECIAL FEATURES

Reviews are straightforward and informative. They provide all the information you need for a pleasurable visit: from clear instructions on how to get there, descriptions of the facilities on offer and the type of catering. Each review also contains a few choice phrases to sum up the character of the place, so discerning guests know exactly what they're getting beforehand.

Solid, no-frills information on an extensive list of places to stay within the British Isles and Eire.

www.Hotelguide.com
Hotel Guide

Overall rating: ★ ★ ★ ★ ★			
Classification: Directory		**Readability:** ★ ★ ★ ★
Updating: Realtime		**Content:** ★ ★ ★ ★ ★
Navigation: ★ ★ ★ ★		**Speed:** ★ ★ ★

SW

This is the largest hotel directory on the internet, where you can find hotels and link to their online booking services by entering either the name of a town or a specific hotel. The site has an exceptionally large and comprehensive listing and although it does feature many deluxe hotels, some of the super deluxe such as The Four Seasons in Milan are not available.

SPECIAL FEATURES

Hotel Discount Card offers between 10 and 30 per cent savings off participating hotel prices for a fee of $42 US (about £25). You can apply for the card online using your credit card, but the only snag is that the website doesn't divulge the nitty gritty of the participant list, although you can email for more information.

This Swiss site reflects that nation's expertise in hotels, and is well worth a visit for keen accommodation hunters.

www.accomodata.com
Accomodata

Overall rating: ★ ★ ★ ★			
Classification: Links		**Readability:**	★ ★ ★ ★
Updating: Daily		**Content:**	★ ★ ★ ★ ★
Navigation: ★ ★ ★ ★		**Speed:**	★ ★ ★

UK

www.ase.net
Hotels and Resorts

Overall rating: ★ ★ ★ ★			
Classification: Search		**Readability:**	★ ★ ★
Updating: Frequently		**Content:**	★ ★ ★ ★
Navigation: ★ ★ ★ ★ ★		**Speed:**	★ ★ ★

UK

To enter this site click on the proudly waving Union Jack on the gateway page — this site is definitely aiming to entice the British consumer. Like many of the hotel and accommodation related websites, the name is misleading. The site offers everything from flight and theatre tickets, to what's on guides and visitor statistics. The accommodation slant is actually more in the site advertising than in the content. A very visually busy site.

To get straight to the accommodation search, click on the smallish Hotels, B&B, Self Catering logo in the centre of the homepage to find a destination index. The links for each destination are impressive.

This search engine will help you to find hotels, bed and breakfasts, resorts, and accommodation websites from around the world. By using a drop-down menu of countries or a separate drop-down menu of US states, you can gain access to a survey of specific requirements. Be prepared to spend some time thinking this through, as the search engine is fairly nosey. Once submitted, a lengthy list of alternatives is usually provided: the site promises 84,500 entries in its database.

The homepage layout is acceptable, but the designers are behind the times with consumer preferences, and there are too many banner ads. Coping with an irritating monkey jumping back and forth at the top of the screen can make you want to leave in a hurry.

www.hotelstravel.com
HotelsTravel

Overall rating: ★ ★ ★ ★			
Classification:	E-agent	Readability:	★ ★ ★
Updating:	Realtime	Content:	★ ★ ★ ★
Navigation:	★ ★ ★	Speed:	★ ★ ★ ★ ★

US

HotelsTravel is a misleading name for what is essentially a full online travel agent giving links to 75,000 lodging and travel-related resources worldwide. Unless you're particularly looking to reserve a hotel, flight, car, or rail pass, the best method to see if HotelsTravel can help is to click on Travel-Related Services to find a fairly straightforward scroll-down site index.

A word of caution: the sites does not provide an 'About Us' page and invites businesses to add their site. This may mean that it's not as controlled as you might like, but in some cases it does fit the bill.

www.leisurehunt.com
Leisurehunt

Overall rating: ★ ★ ★ ★			
Classification:	Search	Readability:	★ ★ ★ ★ ★
Updating:	Regular	Content:	★ ★ ★ ★ ★
Navigation:	★ ★ ★ ★	Speed:	★ ★ ★ ★ ★

UK R

This matter-of-fact, straightforward and speedy service, offers a search by destination for hotels, bed and breakfasts, campsites, hostels, and self-catering. It is a wide-ranging easily navigable site with six choices on the homepage.

SPECIAL FEATURES

Worldwide Accommodation Search by Location allows you to select from five categories, four price levels, and 12 facility specifications (such as wheelchair access, swimming pool, and conference facilities). Quite conveniently, you can choose to have more than one type of accommodation or price category so that you can expand your search range in one search. Coverage of the UK seems to be the most in depth with spot-on results for even the most out-of-the-way locations and good matches to all requests produced. The foreign searches yielded less quantity for rural and suburban destinations, but more than enough for city requests.

Speedbook is for realtime immediate booking for UK accommodation. It has a very good selection, good descriptions and summaries.

A swift and wide-ranging accommodation booking service, most extensive in UK and larger foreign cities, but with vast worldwide listings suiting every budget and facility requirement.

www.beduk.com
B&B my Guest

Overall rating: ★ ★ ★			
Classification:	Guide	Readability:	★ ★ ★ ★
Updating:	Periodically	Content:	★ ★ ★ ★
Navigation:	★ ★ ★ ★ ★	Speed:	★ ★ ★

US

This site is proud of the fact that they were the first complete computer reservation system for Bed and Breakfast establishments in the UK. But despite their claims, online booking is not possible and reservations must be made and confirmed by email.

The site is based in Atlanta and as such, is probably more suited to the US traveller visiting the UK. However it is a great information source and let's face it, Americans usually demand high standards. It's a shame there's no listing for Ireland.

www.country-house-hotels.com
Country House Hotels

Overall rating: ★ ★ ★			
Classification:	Guide	Readability:	★ ★ ★ ★
Updating:	Rarely	Content:	★ ★ ★
Navigation:	★ ★ ★ ★ ★	Speed:	★ ★ ★ ★

UK

A very basic presentation (mostly black print on a white background) divides this guide to country hotels into eleven regions. Although some quality places to stay are offered, the database is not all that extensive, listing only five hotels in the Cotswolds and six in the Lake District. To book, it's necessary to email or telephone the individual hotels.

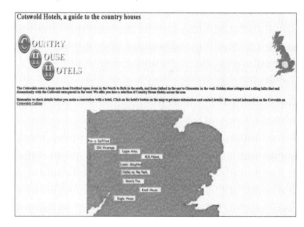

www.privatevillas.com
Private Villas

Overall rating: ★ ★ ★			
Classification:	Guide	**Readability:**	★ ★ ★ ★
Updating:	Rarely	**Content:**	★ ★ ★ ★
Navigation:	★ ★ ★ ★ ★	**Speed:**	★ ★

UK

Not a tour operator and not an agent, Privatevillas puts visitors in touch with villa owners, or small companies offering villa accommodation. Choose from various locations around the world, and then pull up a short description of what the company or individual is offering. Prices range from £300 to £4000 per week. For further details, the telephone number, address, or website address of each property manager is given. It's a rather busy site, but it also gives links to car rental suppliers and flight finders to help you get to your chosen property.

SPECIAL FEATURES

Ski Feature offers chalets to ski buffs.

Property for Sale is directed at the investor looking for a little extra rental income. At the time of review most of the properties appeared to be in Florida, but some were listed for Portugal and Spain. This could be due to America's ease with internet buying and selling, as opposed to the more cautious continental Europeans.

A rather large site, which appears to be neither villa supermarket nor boutique. Nonetheless, it may be just what you are looking for.

OTHER SITES OF INTEREST

Holiday Rentals.com
www.holidayrentals.com
This site is specific to property rentals in the Chamonix-Mont-Blanc area. Owned by an individual, Tim Hall, it actually offers his own studio (for £450 per week) in Les Praz, only 1.5km from Chamonix. Besides that, the site is an excellent source of information for things to do in the area and Tim's photos are very good. Other sites take note!

Holiday Bank
www.holidaybank.co.uk
Although operating as a full agent, one of the best parts of this site is its Private Villa feature, found on the left of the screen's site index, which visitors should note also includes apartments in popular European cities such as Rome and Paris.

Island Hideaways
www.islandhideaways.com
A list of sites specific to villas and houses in the Caribbean.

Spanish Affair
www.spanishaffair.com
Sites specific to villas and houses in Spain

Elysian Holidays
www.elysianholidays.co.uk
(See p. 49)

Boutique and Luxury Hotels

Relais Chateaux
www.relaischateaux.fr
This is an association that unites 426 independently owned hotels and restaurants of charm and prestige in 43 countries around the world. The only problem is that when searching for an establishment, the site uses colour coding with no key provided.

Leading Hotels of the World
www.lhw.com

Design Hotels
www.designhotels.com

Preferred Hotels and Resorts
www.preferredhotels.com

Hilton Hotels
www.hilton.com

Sheraton Hotels
www.sheraton.com

Mandarin Oriental
www.mandarin-oriental.com

The Savoy Group
www.savoy-group.co.uk

Orient Express Hotels
www.orient-expresshotels.com

The Ritz London
www.theritzhotel.co.uk

The Lanesborough
www.lanesborough.co.uk

Raffles International
www.raffleshotel.com

Meridien Forte Hotels
www.forte-hotels.com

Ritz Carlton
www.ritzcarlton.com

Siolim House Goa
www.siolimhouse

Banyan Tree Resorts
www.banyantree.com

Chapter 4

special interest travel

'There's a famous seaside place called Blackpool,
That's noted for fresh air and fun'

Marriott Edgar (1932)

Just as an artist needs a muse, occasionally travellers need some inspiration. The following list of sites serves not only as an efficient and convenient way to book a holiday, but also as a collection of ideas which can be perused for recreation. There are so many special places in the world that offer so much, and although previously the traveller has been dependent on a kind travel agent to put forward interesting ideas, now it's possible to see for oneself all that's available. And, of course, it's not only Blackpool that's noted for fun.

Adventure and activities

The following sites prove that there is more to life than sunbathing whilst on holiday. Using the following sites you can find any type of special interest holiday, from archaeology to wine tasting. The more adventurous amongst you can find walking, sailing, kayaking or bungee jumping. In fact it is amazing to see what some people do for a bit of relaxation!

www.rainbowadventures.com
Adventure Women

Overall rating: ★ ★ ★ ★

Classification:	Tour Operator	**Readability:**	★ ★ ★ ★ ★
Updating:	Regularly	**Content:**	★ ★ ★ ★ ★
Navigation:	★ ★ ★ ★ ★	**Speed:**	★ ★ ★ ★ ★

US

AdventureWomen is an eighteen-year-old business and its attractive site, filled with a lot of text and fun icons, sells its own extraordinarily exotic adventure trips for women. The trips are so interesting and well-planned that it is well worth the time to browse through the detailed descriptions that are available by email. Booking requests are by e-mail or telephone, and response times to queries are almost immediate. The site and the business are based in the US, but the holidays can be booked from anywhere in the world.

SPECIAL FEATURES

Are you an AdventureWoman? is a good place to start. It summarises the AdventureWomen customer profile, and explores the meaning of the term adventure holiday. This in itself makes for entertaining reading!

Trips for 2000 links to details of the well-selected trips, which include Montana skiing clinics, riding in Ireland, sea kayaking in Mexico, windjammer sailing in the British Virgin Islands, hiking the Havasupai reservation in the Grand Canyon, mini-jaunts to the French Riviera, rafting the Colorado River through the Grand Canyon, and a boat tour of Burgundy. The site replies instantly to requests by sending an email including complete details of each trip, itinerary, costs, skills required, packing, and visas. This is a nice touch of efficiency and helps to keep the site working smoothly.

High Adventure Series links to the liveliest part of the site. Each year, Adventure Women organises three especially challenging trips in three categories of challenge: cultural, ecological and physical. For the year 2000, these were to Timbuktu, the Amazon River, and Alaska. This page scrolls down with enticing photos and descriptions of the three trips and also provides costs, dates and an email option for more details. The email response service is almost instantaneous. As an example of the high calibre of the trips and the service, the Timbuktu trip details include a well-written history of Mali and its people and geography. The odyssey across Mali offers an exploration of desert landscapes, a visit to the sandcastle city of Djenee, travel by pinase (riverboat) down the Niger River camping on the Niger river banks, studies and observation of the dance, ceremonies of the Dogon people, and riding camels to a nomadic Tuareg encampment. And there's much more.

Press Clippings combines a listing of accolades for and reviews of the site as well as some great articles by Adventure Women clients describing the actual trips. Again, good reading for insight into the type of adventures and clientele.

A pleasant and cheerful site selling extraordinary adventure trips for women.

www.activehols.co.uk
Cinammon Adventure

Overall rating: ★ ★ ★ ★ ★			
Classification:	Tour Operator	**Readability:**	★ ★ ★ ★ ★
Updating:	Regularly	**Content:**	★ ★ ★ ★ ★
Navigation:	★ ★ ★ ★	**Speed:**	★ ★ ★ ★ ★

UK

The Cinnamon Adventure site has an uncluttered homepage with a menu bar leading directly to a grand assortment of corporate, family, group or individual adventure and fun holidays in the UK and France. The homepage also features a neat listing of holidays in the near future, for last minute getaways. This company has adventure markets very well-covered, but the site is still most useful for those seeking a holiday in the UK. Boasting tailor-made holidays with favourite activities to be combined with a preferred location, this site offers lots of flexibility and plenty of opportunity to express preferences clearly, with no boxes to fill in. Checking availability can be done by email, but actual booking is by phone.

SPECIAL FEATURES

Groups is for arranging adventure holidays for groups of six to ten people. A regional UK map is provided, and a quick click on the region of choice connects to a page with a lengthy list of options and program descriptions. To move onto booking, click the 'check availability' icon at the bottom of the Groups page, fill in the email form, and the process is started.

Corporate is not only good for large corporations, but also for small businesses, as it offers team activities for groups of between four and 100 people. The choices are clearly explained and the range is colossal, with traditional corporate outings like clay pigeon shooting, skiing, fishing, racing, and sailing as well as more unlikely activities like 'sheep communiqué', which involves blindfolding humans and sheep. There are also appealing team outings involving helicopters, armoured personnel carriers, and speedboats. Look out 007!

Families leads to the over-12 family activity holidays, just perfect for teenagers who want to do something challenging without being surrounded by whining younger kids. Because of the age limit, the activities can be truly challenging: parents participate fully! Cinnamon runs these family holidays in a two-star country hotel in Wales. The activities include white water rafting on the Tryweryn River, Canadian canoeing, abseiling, mountain biking in the Forest of North Wales, and invigorating adventure walks through water pools and over boulders.

Adventure in Store is a unique UK shopping site which offers send-a-friend 'adrenaline vouchers'. These vouchers, offer a 10% discount for those booking a holiday.

This is one of the top sites for UK adventure holidays, for both the individual and groups.

www.complete-skier.com
Complete-skier

Overall rating: ★ ★ ★ ★ ★			
Classification:	Search	**Readability:**	★ ★ ★ ★ ★
Updating:	Regularly	**Content:**	★ ★ ★ ★
Navigation:	★ ★ ★ ★ ★	**Speed:**	★ ★ ★ ★ ★

UK

This is the ultimate skier's website. It features several hundred thousand ski holiday possibilities at resorts all over the world, ski news, snow reports, multiple webcams, well-written features on every aspect of skiing, and related information. The centre of the homepage is a bit cluttered with specific holiday offers, but on either side are clear choice click-aways. And guess what? There's online booking! Alternatively, you can use the telephone.

SPECIAL FEATURES

Travel Centre at the top of the homepage leads visitors directly to a powerful all-requirements search facility to look for accommodation, flights, car rentals, travel insurance, a currency converter, a page on driving in ski areas and top links to several informational ski sites. There is an immense worldwide selection of chalets, apartments, hotels, and hostels for a variety of budgets. Also featured is a Discount Holiday Booking Service which offers some spectacular deals, such as a week in Verbier or Wengen, including flights for £389, or a week in Stowe, Vermont, including flights for £439.

Resort is useful for those interested in specific resort information or needing to learn about unknown resorts. Resort Wizard is an accurate matchmaker, providing personality analysis to determine whether the resort-seekers are party animals, romantics, family people, or penny-pinchers (all with specified skiing abilities and geographical preferences) amongst others. The Resort page also houses a link to Rascal, which is advertised to be the most powerful resort finder on the web. It takes a bit of playing around to come up with the right resort here, as there are dozens of options for specifications: extent of snowmaking, number of mountain restaurants, ice skating rinks and more. The more specific the search, the less likely it is to turn up resort rubbish. There isn't a best efforts function and it is also a bit slow.

Our Resort Recommendations is the most agile and quick resort finder found on the Resort page. It is the Complete-Skier's own recommendations and allows the visitor to choose one category at a time (such as best vertical drop, best for families, best après-ski, beginners, telemark, heliski, most halfpipes), and quickly yields a list of 10-20 resorts to click onto for more details.

Links connects to a summary ski directory, which includes all the resorts accessible from the rest of the site, but also links to sites on health, special needs, ski associations, personals pages, other directories and lots of mountain webcams. This would definitely be a good pre-ski or pre-booking stopoff.

An enticing site which allows visitors to plan a ski holiday with minimal MEGO (my eyes glazed over) factor!

www.fieldingtravel.com/df/
Fielding's Dangerfinder

Overall rating: ★ ★ ★ ★

Classification:	Guide	Readability:	★ ★ ★ ★
Updating:	Regularly	Content:	★ ★ ★ ★ ★
Navigation:	★ ★ ★ ★	Speed:	★ ★ ★ ★ ★

US

Based on Fielding's fastest-selling travel guide, Fielding's Dangerous Places, this site has a nice basic homepage which is clearly organised and straightforward to use. The lists of Adventure Calls or Adventure Clubs lead to extensive and well-written sections divided by interest. This site contains a lot of information for those who are interested in joining non-profit experiences like science expeditions, working for a relief agency, or travelling through a war zone. It also lists adventure travel specialists for holiday travel to dangerous places and gives the best-ever practical advice for danger travelling.

SPECIAL FEATURES

Adventure Calls gives links to adventure trips, expeditions, adventure and travel information, volunteer vacations, and web resources for those working overseas.

Blackflag Café is an active and lively forum for hardcore danger travellers and adventurers. The letters have a good number of local correspondents from dangerous places offering tips based on experience.

An outstanding mix of information, free from commercial taint, for the most adventurous travellers.

www.highplaces.co.uk
High Places

Overall rating: ★ ★ ★ ★ ★			
Classification: Guide		**Readability:**	★ ★ ★ ★ ★
Updating: Regularly		**Content:**	★ ★ ★ ★ ★
Navigation: ★ ★ ★ ★		**Speed:**	★ ★ ★

UK

The site begins by modestly presenting only three options: treks, general information, or request a brochure. Don't be misled by the paucity of choices; there is a much bigger mountain on the other side of each click. This UK-based company gives all the necessary information on the friendly and informal treks, hikes, climbs, and ski-tours it offers in high places throughout the world. In one trip, travellers can ascend a 5016 foot volcano and then visit the headwaters of the Amazon in Ecuador; in another, the famous Wadi Rum in Jordan is explored on foot and by camel. The tours take place on every continent and are described in detail, giving day-by-day itineraries, difficulty levels, departure dates, and accommodation notes. There are some attractive photographs. Brochures and detailed trek information can be ordered online, but booking is by phone.

SPECIAL FEATURES

General Info and People in High Places allows potential trekkers to meet the staff and guides of High Places. One can't help but be impressed with how well-trained and well-travelled they are.

This site gives fully global choices for serious trekking combined with some lowland interest and visits.

www.ranchweb.com
Ranchweb

Overall rating: ★ ★ ★ ★ ★			
Classification: Brochure		**Readability:**	★ ★ ★ ★ ★
Updating: Regularly		**Content:**	★ ★ ★ ★ ★
Navigation: ★ ★ ★ ★		**Speed:**	★ ★ ★ ★ ★

US R

Yee ha cowboy! This worldwide ranch headquarters site was founded by Gene Kilgore, author of the best-selling book *Gene Kilgore's Ranch Vacations - The Complete Guide to Guest and Resort, Fly-fishing and Country Skiing Ranches*. The site is an exciting guide that definitely inspires you to get right out on the trail. Once that's decided there are over a hundred ways to do it including yoga, wagon trips, rock climbing, Native American interest, naturalist, rodeo, luxury, and special tours for big or heavy riders. There are also hundreds of ranch locations including one in Mongolia. The site lists each ranch with a thoroughly descriptive write-up providing all the necessary information, including phone numbers for booking. There is also a worldwide ranch and lodge interactive map. The site is easily trawlable and understandable.

SPECIAL FEATURES

Travel launches directly into ranch definitions and selection and then allows browsing by travel category or ranch type (executive conference, dude, working cattle, family etc). From Travel one can also link to the excellent For Kids and Travel Specials pages with substantially discounted holiday offers.

Definitely worth a good long look for anybody considering a ranch holiday or wanting to learn about ranches and ranching.

www.regal-diving.co.uk
Regal's Red Sea and World Wide Holidays

Overall rating: ★ ★ ★ ★ ★			
Classification:	Tour Operator	**Readability:**	★ ★ ★ ★ ★
Updating:	Regularly	**Content:**	★ ★ ★ ★ ★
Navigation:	★ ★ ★ ★ ★	**Speed:**	★ ★ ★ ★ ★

UK

This tropical-coloured, easy to navigate site summarises the alluring diving holidays offered by Regal's, twice Best Dive Tour Operator of the Year award winner. Holidays suit every level of diving expertise from novice to experienced. There are also diving holidays offered for families with children of all ages. Most of the holidays take place in the Red Sea area, in Jordan and Israel. Booking is by telephone.

SPECIAL FEATURES

Learn to Dive lists Regal's selection of resorts and courses for those hoping to learn to dive. Not sure if diving is for you? There's a free try-dive option which has a no-quibble money-back guarantee if you decide not to follow through with the course.

Activity Selector helps with selecting a destination. Lists of facilities and activities offered are listed such as living on a boat above one's chosen diving area, sharks, billiards, snorkelling, marine life, wrecks, and windsurfing.

A great site for anybody who hasn't seen the film Jaws.

www.serioussports.com
Serioussports

Overall rating: ★ ★ ★ ★ ★			
Classification:	Directory	**Readability:**	★ ★ ★ ★ ★
Updating:	Regularly	**Content:**	★ ★ ★ ★ ★
Navigation:	★ ★ ★ ★	**Speed:**	★ ★ ★ ★ ★

US R

This is a prodigious directory and information site for outdoor and adventure sports outfitters, guides and schools. SeriousSports stands out for the distinctive top quality holidays and services that it offers. It is not easy to get a company listed here, and only the best warrant a full description on the site. Companies are required to have been operating for three years, be properly accredited, have received strong positive press reviews as well as be approved by a panel of field experts.

Linked pages are presented in SeriousSport's pleasant branded lilac-blue designer format but the really user-friendly point is that jumps back to the homepage from the links are quick and easy. Most of the listings are US-based and present a snappy wrap-up of the US opportunities. The international listings are sparse by location, but offer the full range of activities.

SeriousSports is very easy to navigate, despite there being no site map. Sports and holidays are listed by category and destination with direct links to the travel companies, schools, outfitters and venues. SeriousSports also has a highly informative newsletter, although registration is required for this. In general the site offers high-grade, quality information although it might benefit from a search facility allowing visitors to select by ability, budget, or other criteria.

SPECIAL FEATURES

Air Sports links to listings of hang gliding, paragliding, skydiving and soaring holidays, resorts, facilities and schools. There is a search by region facility with US regions and then states, but the international search puts the whole non-US world together in a rather short index. Some 'temporary listings' are not in the SeriousSports branded format, but are designed in a white page and typed listing format.

Land Sports leads you to choices for rock climbing, mountaineering, Western vacations (Western US) and horse trekking as well as outdoor skills schools, multi-activity programs and other sports. Here there are opportunities to stay at a real non-holiday ranch, to trek through the backwoods of West Virginia while a llama carries your luggage and tent, or to sign up for a snowshoe-making or advanced wilderness first aid course. Again, these are really the most top-notch links, award-winning holiday companies, award-winning holidays, and the best schools and training centres.

Water Sports is the page for those interested in sailing schools, kayaking (ocean, sea, and river), canoeing, fishing and white water rafting. There is a strong section for family holidays with older children (white water rafting and camping while someone else does the cooking and lugging might be just the recipe for family bonding). The sailing schools listed offer serious sailing with exhaustive curricula: celestial navigation, ocean passage making, zero visibility coastal passage making, J80 Asymetrical for closing speeds in excess of 20 knots, racing camp, and good old basic keelboating.

Jump takes you directly to your favourite sport or region, or to the search option.

An impressive and enjoyable adventure sports guide and directory.

www.sherpa-walking-holidays.co.uk
Sherpa Expeditions Online

Overall rating: ★ ★ ★ ★			
Classification:	Tour Operator	**Readability:**	★ ★ ★ ★ ★
Updating:	Regularly	**Content:**	★ ★ ★ ★ ★
Navigation:	★ ★ ★ ★	**Speed:**	★ ★ ★ ★

UK R

Sherpa Expeditions has enough choices to keep any walker or cyclist going for several decades. The homepage offers a choice of self-guided or escorted trips and then a further choice by worldwide destination. Click on Holidays on the homepage, and then Search for a Holiday, to be presented with a powerful search facility. The choices range from region, duration, difficulty level, and type. Options pop up quickly and link to full holiday details for each choice.

SPECIAL FEATURES

Preparation presents a very helpful grading system used for categorising cycling and walking difficulty levels. Unfortunately for some, it then goes on to describe the fitness level required for each.

OTHER FEATURES

There is also a free newsletter, the opportunity to download self-guided tour notes, and access to the community section, which offers a message board, press cuttings, screensavers, and client feedback. Make sure to read the usually boring, but here fascinating, About Us and Press Cuttings which detail Sherpa's unique background and success.

Look here for a truly comprehensive selection of walking and cycling holidays and expeditions, both guided and for the lone explorer.

www.acornactivities.co.uk
Acornactivities

Overall rating: ★ ★ ★ ★			
Classification:	Tour Operator	**Readability:**	★ ★ ★ ★ ★
Updating:	Regularly	**Content:**	★ ★ ★ ★ ★
Navigation:	★ ★ ★ ★	**Speed:**	★ ★ ★ ★

UK

Once past the bookcover and into the main site, those seeking a UK-based activity holiday will certainly not be disappointed. It is a simple process to find any activity, and holidays by the thousands are listed, all neatly categorised and accessible: accelerated freefalls, Charles Rennie Mackintosh days, drystone walling, Formula One driving, rush seating, tandem skydiving, Lotus Elise experience, murder mystery, survival, water sports, and more. There are also special arrangements for hen and stag weekends, for instance scuba diving and paintballing. Gift vouchers can be bought and brochures can be ordered. Bookings are online, by telephone or email.

This site is a one-stop shop for fun activities in the UK for families, groups, and individuals.

www.safarilink.com
Safari Link

Overall rating: ★ ★ ★			
Classification:	Search	**Readability:**	★ ★ ★ ★ ★
Updating:	Regularly	**Content:**	★ ★ ★ ★ ★
Navigation:	★ ★ ★ ★	**Speed:**	★ ★ ★ ★ ★

UK

This search engine connects with what would otherwise be a very fragmented and hard-to-access market. Accordingly, you are kick-started by a semi-compulsory yet speedily answered search as soon as the homepage unfurls. After wrestling with this, small but deceptive side alleys must be negotiated before the required information is found. After a little while you get the hang of it and can start to take advantage of all that Africa has to offer. The linked pages are branded and allow you to hop back to the Safari Link home page with ease.

As with many search engines, the facility works best with specific words such as gorilla, rather than vague terms like African wildlife. One or two words will suffice when filling in the search fields, and not all the boxes need to be completed.

For game-mad people, this site offers a safari search engine that reaches parts no one else can.

www.infohub.com		
InfoHub		
Overall rating: ★ ★ ★		
Classification: Guide	**Readability:**	★ ★ ★ ★ ★
Updating: Regularly	**Content:**	★ ★ ★ ★ ★
Navigation: ★ ★ ★ ★	**Speed:**	★ ★ ★ ★ ★
US		

Infohub is a directory of the world's largest collections of adventure, art, learning, and sport vacations. The list is endless, with several hundred categories of activities such as camel riding, nudist resorts, elephant polo, lesbian tours, ice climbing, hot springs, volcano tours, rollerblading tours, and many more conventional sorts of fun. The site is easily toured by a search facility incorporating choices from the front page scroll-down menus of destination, activity, travel period, and price. The choice can be intimidating, but fortunately the size of the site does not mean the holidays are mass production deals; there are lots of boutique offerings available. Requests and bookings are by email.

SPECIAL FEATURES

Tour Gallery lets you select by tour activity type, gives you a worldwide listing of tours in that category and then gives you the option to investigate similar tours by type, destination, and date. Once a holiday has been decided upon, full brochure details and availability information can be obtained by email.

Links leads to passport information, worldwide limousine services, and the like.

Infohub is a great site for travellers who are looking for, or who may have run out of, ideas.

Sailing Holidays

Paradise Adventures
www.paradiseadventures.com.au/worldwidesailing.htm

Admiralty Yacht Vacations
www.admirals.com

Saltyseas.com
www.saltyseas.com

Sailing Holidays
www.sailing-holidays.net

Fishing Holidays

Go Fishing Worldwide
www.go-fishing-worldwide.com/Go-Fishing-Ww/

Worldwide Fishing Adventures
www.wheretofish.com

Fishing in France
www.fishinginfrance.com

Golf Holidays

Destination Golf
www.destinationgolf.co.uk

3D Golf
www.3dgolf.co.uk

Dolphin and Whale Holidays

Dolphin Excursions
www.dolphinexcursions.com

The Divine Dolphin
www.divinedolphin.com/dolphinswim.htm

Dolphin Watch
www.dolphinwatch.com.au

Whale Song
www.whalesong.com.au

Whalemans Dolphin & Whale Eco-adventure Travel
www.whaleadventures.com

Miscellaneous Holidays

France In Your Glass
www.inyourglass.com
Upmarket vineyard touring holidays in France.

Saga
www.saga.co.uk
Imaginative holidays for the over 50's.

Ecovolunteer
www.ecovolunteer.com
Fancy studying the Bluenose Dolphin in Italy or assisting researchers in an Elephant camp in Cameroon? Then look into these working holidays for the ecologically minded.

Art History Abroad
www.arthistoryabroad.com
Modern grand tours of Italy for gap year students and adult culture vultures.

Tasting Places
www.tastingplaces.com
Culinary holidays in Italy and Thailand.

Italian Cookery Weeks
www.italian-cookery-weeks.co.uk
Cooking holidays in the heart of Italy

www.explore.co.uk
Explore World Wide

Email brochure request service detailing tons and tons of adventure holidays in various locations.

Spa Sites

For those slightly less adventurous souls who feel that life has become too tiring and toxic, the following sites will provide an inspirational list of spas, which aim to reduce that weary feeling. The sites make it easy for you to compare and find what is ideal for you, whether it be chanting in a monastery on a hill or lying on puffed up cushy towels with cucumber slices cooling your tired eyes.

www.worldhealthspa.com
World Health Spa Directory

Overall rating: ★ ★ ★ ★

Classification:	Directory	Readability:	★ ★ ★ ★ ★
Updating:	Regularly	Content:	★ ★ ★ ★ ★
Navigation:	★ ★ ★ ★ ★	Speed:	★ ★ ★ ★ ★

UK

The World Health Spa Directory proffers a tantalising selection of calm and therapeutic oases worldwide. Click Enter on the homepage to leap into a text-dense yet easy-to-use index, where you'll be faced with the choice of reading about spas, browsing through spa details, or learning about treatment definitions. There is also access to heaps of customer reviews, and long features with pictures of the spas. The site is concerned with much more than merely facials, focusing as it does on the spa lifestyle of spirituality, sexuality, and reiki as much as hot tubs, slimming, and good old creams and cosmetics. There's a good mix of non-cloying reviews and well-organised searches. Although the site is run from the UK, the shopping is US-based.

SPECIAL FEATURES

Directory allows you to search for spas by type and location. How about computerised ancient royal treatments at the top of the Andes Mountains or natural hot sand bathing in Japan? This could be very useful for booking a day of rest and relaxation when on a business or holiday trip.

Those with tired eyes and weary feet should bookmark this page for a bit of relaxation.

www.spafinder.com
Spafinder

Overall rating: ★ ★ ★ ★			
Classification: E-agent		**Readability:**	★ ★ ★ ★
Updating: Regularly		**Content:**	★ ★ ★ ★ ★
Navigation: ★ ★ ★ ★		**Speed:**	★ ★ ★

US

www.thermalia.co.uk
Thermalia Travel

Overall rating: ★ ★ ★ ★			
Classification: E-agent		**Readability:**	★ ★ ★ ★ ★
Updating: Regularly		**Content:**	★ ★ ★ ★ ★
Navigation: ★ ★ ★ ★ ★		**Speed:**	★ ★ ★ ★

UK

Spafinder is run by the world's largest spa travel and marketing company, but the site has the low-key, efficient feel of a luxury reception area. Fresh, unwrinkled faces peer at you from the screen as you browse the various categories. The last minute specials are very impressive, including the Golden Door in California with herbal wraps and 'wake-up' walks (before a cup of coffee, no less). Movement between pages is a bit slow, but the massive amount of information is well controlled and trafficked. The shopping is US-based. Online booking is available for residents of all countries, although prices are given in dollars.

SPECIAL FEATURES

Spa Search gives information on various spas and how to book. The retreats and getaways are priced in dollars and air arrangements can be requested separately if necessary. The range is astounding, especially as it is not just a guide, but a booker. Searching is a bit unwieldy at first but with some helpful computer suggestions, you get there in the end.

Cuisine is a gem of a page, with recipes from spas famous for their cuisine. Each spa was asked to give one of their favourite recipes and they all seem to be on the cutting edge: delicious, non-fattening food in a range of styles. Fantastic!

This site is a must for anyone wanting a spa holiday.

Thermalia is a UK-based holiday company offering retreats to a select group of spas in Europe, Asia, and Africa. The spas all offer thermal therapies that are particularly suitable for people with chronic rheumatism, arthritis, or over-used joints. Booking requests are made online and the company return the call. The site is big on detailed explanations: modern stress, various therapies, and the health-restoring benefits of a healthy break. The resorts are thoroughly described and the special offers are well arranged and well priced.

SPECIAL FEATURES

Therapies/glossary explains all the different thermal therapies including fangotherapy, Scottish shower, and balneotherapy. Select a preferred treatment and up pops the list of spas where it's on offer.

A useful site for anybody suffering from any type of rheumatic illness.

Business Travel

These sites are specifically designed to help the business traveller, and tends to focus on travel for The Suit. It aims to put all the information a business traveller might want, at their fingertips.

www.business-travel.co.uk
Business Travel Plus

Overall rating: ★ ★ ★ ★

Classification:	E-agent	**Readability:**	★ ★ ★ ★
Updating:	Regularly	**Content:**	★ ★ ★ ★
Navigation:	★ ★ ★ ★	**Speed:**	★ ★ ★ ★ ★

UK

Business Travel Plus is the website of a UK-based travel management service. It's a basic but very well-functioning site, bonded by IATA, ABTA, and ATOL. You can use the site for special offers and timetable searches, but businesses benefit from a skilled back-up team offering all aspects of business travel management including account management, itinerary arrange-ments, and corporate events.

Generally this site is best used as an introduction to British Travel Plus services. It also suits BTP's existing business clients.

OTHER SITES OF INTEREST

World Executive Hotel directory
www.worldexecutive.com

Sapphire Executive Chauffeurs Limited
www.executive-travel.co.uk

Connect Globally, Mobile Computer Solutions
www.connectglobally.com

Laptop Travel
www.laptoptravel.com

Family Travel

There's nothing worse for a parent than cringing in a hotel when their toddler throws his plastic cup on the floor, and all eyes turn to accompany the disapproving silence. The following sites help parents to plan travel that will suit them, and their children, whatever their age. These sites truly are helpful for planning a holiday for families.

www.ski-esprit.co.uk & www.sun-esprit.co.uk
Ski Esprit/Sun Esprit

Overall rating: ★ ★ ★ ★

Classification:	Tour Operator	Readability:	★ ★ ★ ★ ★
Updating:	Regularly	Content:	★ ★ ★ ★ ★
Navigation:	★ ★ ★ ★	Speed:	★ ★ ★ ★

UK

Sun and Ski Esprit present pictures and tempting descriptions of their quality family alpine holidays. They seem to be attempting to achieve the magical mix of marital and juvenile satisfaction, and promise that 'parents can still enjoy some of the things they did before...'. Booking is by phone, but the site provides a good starting point for planning a holiday. They are ABTA, ATOL, and AITO members, with a Child Care Guarantee. The Ski Esprit site has more pre-holiday and tourism information than Sun Esprit, but both sites successfully give potential holidaymakers a clear vision of the services and resorts available. Each site has a clear homepage with important links made obvious.

SPECIAL FEATURES

Resorts/Our Resorts has maps and descriptions of each resort that link separately to further information and pictures of the locations in the Swiss and French Alps.

Contact Us has all the necessary contact numbers, addresses, industry bondings, and guarantees.

These cheerful and concise UK travel company sites offer winter and summer Alpine holidays which aim to pamper every member of the family.

www.disney.co.uk/usa-resorts
Disney's USA Resorts

Overall rating: ★ ★ ★ ★			
Classification:	Information	Readability:	★ ★ ★ ★ ★
Updating:	Monthly	Content:	★ ★ ★ ★
Navigation:	★ ★ ★ ★ ★	Speed:	★ ★ ★ ★ ★

UK

Like its sister site, disneylandparis.com, the USA Resorts site is found under the main disney.co.uk umbrella homepage. It's directed towards the British tourist who wants to go further afield to experience Disney and presents pages on Walt Disney World Resort in Florida, Disneyland in California and Disney's Cruise Lines. There are also additional pages for information on booking, itinerary planning and even packing.

SPECIAL FEATURES

Holiday Planning Video is a slightly misleading link title as rather than presenting an online video it merely provides a telephone number for ordering. The video is free, however.

Hot Tips is listed by resort, and provides extremely helpful bits of information such as when USA national holidays are, (so you can book to avoid crowds), and check-in and out times of the hotels.

Like its site relations, this one is easy to use and a must for those considering a family trip to the USA.

www.disneylandparis.com/uk/home.html
Disneyland Paris

Overall rating: ★ ★ ★ ★			
Classification:	Information	Readability:	★ ★ ★ ★ ★
Updating:	Monthly	Content:	★ ★ ★ ★
Navigation:	★ ★ ★ ★ ★	Speed:	★ ★ ★ ★ ★

UK

As part of the huge Disneyland umbrella site disneylandparis.com operates its own magical and easy-to-use subsite. It provides details about the theme park, accommodation, Disney village, the kid's area and the convention centre. The site allows you to plan a trip to Disneyland and decide where to spend your time, before you depart. Reservation requests can be made by email, if you already know the hotel, and the options you prefer. A reservations agent will then contact you as soon as possible to confirm availability and price.

SPECIAL FEATURES

Fastpass is a parent's dream. Details of the Fastpass are found in the centre of the site's homepage where it explains that the pass is a time saving service meant to shorten your waiting time at some of the more popular attractions. The only drawback is that the site doesn't say how one gets one of these highly valued passes.

360 Degree Photographs presents pictures of hotel rooms in each of the park's 7 themed hotels making it much easier to decide which accommodation to choose.

Most families at some point have to take the Disney plunge and this site makes it appear slightly less overwhelming for the apprehensive parents.

http://family.go.com/Categories/Travel
Family.com

Overall rating: ★ ★ ★ ★			
Classification:	Information	**Readability:**	★ ★ ★ ★ ★
Updating:	Regularly	**Content:**	★ ★ ★ ★ ★
Navigation:	★ ★ ★ ★ ★	**Speed:**	★ ★ ★

US

This subsection of the hugely successful Family.com site is like a women's magazine cover with each article title and lead tempting the reader. It is chock-full of all sorts of travel information: destination descriptions, readers' travel experiences and advice, holiday deals, health, and other practical help for those travelling with families. There are also links with Disney for Disney holidays and other information. The page is cheerful and clearly presented, but the mass of information on the site seems to slow down navigation. The short wait is worth the quality of the upbeat and straightforward writing by travel and health experts.

SPECIAL FEATURES

Travel Planner presents a destination and holiday type (day trip, museum, outdoor, cruise, beach, theme park) menu which link to listings of holiday destinations, deals and related information. To get the most out of this page scroll down to the strangely placed 'type of vacation' choice at the bottom of the page. Here one finds 'advice' which leads to a big choice of help articles and links. Under the location choice, most of the listings are in the United States, but if you scroll down to the end of the US listings, you will find 'international', where there is a fantastic selection of information. There's loads on children in Paris, London, Canada and the Virgin Islands. This page also links to Disney's site.

The United States listings under Travel Planner are extensive. Some of the pastimes listed are truly American and fairly insightful for Europeans. Listings include corn mazes, Baseball Hall of Fame, local river trips, fairs , rodeos, science holidays, the Grand Canyon, National Parks, dog sledding, and skiing. There is also a vast amount of practical help.

Road-tested Vacations is also a super-duper page that can really help parents organise and plan family trips in the US. It contains visitor-written site rankings and descriptions of hundreds of holidays. The reviews are edited and put into a standard format by Family.com and include costs, coolest souvenir, how to get there, what the kids liked and what we liked, and what we didn't like. All readers are invited to share their experiences on the site and there are hundreds of parent-contributed pieces.

Family City Guides lets you choose a major US city and then presents a 'family-friendly city guide' site, where a smart and cheery page lists must-sees, city information, nearby getaways, family dining, and readers' ratings. This is excellent for preparing to visit a specific city and using it as a base for exploration.

A fun, upbeat and highly useful site for family travel, mainly US but some international.

www.families.co.uk
Families.co.uk

Overall rating: ★ ★ ★ ★			
Classification:	Information	**Readability:**	★ ★ ★ ★ ★
Updating:	Periodically	**Content:**	★ ★ ★ ★
Navigation:	★ ★ ★ ★ ★	**Speed:**	★ ★ ★ ★ ★

(UK)

Whilst operating with the right idea, of presenting travel information to those travelling with children, in mind this site would benefit from a little further development. A few more direct links would be really useful, as well as more content. However, even in its current state, it can be helpful to frustrated parents.

Families.co.uk offers three pages of information relating to travel. Family Holidays which focuses on ski holidays and residential camps for children, Travel which provides a short list of travel related websites and Family Hotels which presents a brief list of children friendly hotels in the UK.

The real plus is the easy-peasy navigation combined with smooth readability.

SPECIAL FEATURES

Residential Camps provides a list of UK residential camps that could be for you if your children need a variety of sporting and other interests to keep them happy and are of the appropriate ages. Unfortunately, the list doesn't link to the camp's websites, but telephone numbers are given. This page can be found by clicking on Family Holidays on the homepage.

Skiing Holidays also found under Family Holidays on the homepage, covers family friendly skiing holidays in Europe.

The website designers have assumed that all families wish to fly to their destinations and because of having children, require short transfer times. The ski holidays feature works through using the Top Ten Resorts menu, found at the very bottom of the homepage, where a list of five resorts is presented but unfortunately there aren't yet direct links to tour operators or travel agents to get the whole thing organised.

Tour Operators found at the bottom of the Family Holidays page, offers a drop down menu of three family-oriented tour operators which include Mark Warner, Neilson and Ski Famille with direct links to their websites.

Football Training in France sounds like a great idea. This offers a telephone number for Eurocamp who aim to train boys and girls in football methods and typically they will train for two hours a day. The only drawback is that the site doesn't say if the football training is done in English or if it is expected to be a French language immersion course at the same time.

Overall this site can provide useful bits of information although not as much as one would hope.

OTHER SITES OF INTEREST

Centerparcs
www.centerparcs.com

Mark Warner Holidays
www.markwarner.co.uk (see p. 51)

Women's Travel

The following are sites with information for women travellers. There are tips on where to travel, stay, eat and what to pack, as well as excellent links to shopping sites for those with a propensity to consume.

Some of the information is handy for men as well, so don't feel it's a complete waste of time to visit if your jolly involves a bloke.

www.journeywoman.com
Journeywoman

Overall rating: ★ ★ ★ ★ ★			
Classification:	Ezine	Readability:	★ ★ ★ ★ ★
Updating:	Regularly	Content:	★ ★ ★ ★ ★
Navigation:	★ ★ ★ ★	Speed:	★ ★ ★ ★ ★

CAN R

This is an excellent and extensive travel magazine designed for and written by women, although it's certainly useful and interesting to men as well. It gives quick access to a vast amount of well-organised, well-researched travel information, much of it provided by the local residents of travel or dream destinations, who are often professional writers. The site is superior to others with high subscriber participation as it edits the published contributions, so that clarity and practicality reign throughout. The no-nonsense, no-drivel content is refreshing. Although the site claims to be subscription only, no payment is required.

SPECIAL FEATURES

Free Newsletter gives visitors the opportunity to subscribe to the newsletter and summarises other benefits of subscription; for example, a discount on placement of classified ads, and use of the HERmail.net email system.

Gal-Friendly City Sites offers personal recommendations for hotels, restaurants, sights, shopping, and neighbourhood tours, from correspondents all over the world. The Notes and Numbers local references section is particularly strong. Although the site doesn't cover every city in the world, it does a great job.

Travel Classifieds provides links to a huge range of quality travel opportunities for women, such as learning holidays, bookstores, Ms Biz (for travelling businesswomen), adventure holidays, international home trading, and much more.

Journey Doctor contains highly practical, well-presented and professional medical articles that are independently researched by Journeywoman Online. Subject themes include jet lag, PMS, natural remedies on the road, travel insurance, low-cal travel snacks, and emergencies.

Travel 101 gives advice and tips from professional travel writers on the top ten travel books, the top twenty-five things to put in your backpack, and more.

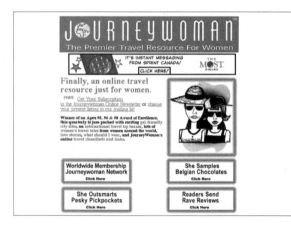

Women Helping Women Travel links to a free site designed especially to put women travellers in touch with one another. Its main purpose is to connect women travelling to a certain destination with women living in that area.

What Should I Wear? gives a summary of recommended clothes for specific destinations. Subscribers are invited to email in their experiences and advice for others to read.

Best Books is one of the best travel book listings ever! Independently listed and reviewed by Journeywoman, it includes good gift lists and well-written reviews. The site sells only to Canadian addresses, but visitors from other countries can still benefit greatly from the lists.

The Older Adventuress is a space for women over fifty, with links to top travel and other sites, as well as practical and philosophical notes from well-travelled adventuresses.

Her Spa Stop and Her Ecoadventures give subscribers frank and fresh personal reviews of spas and ecoadventures worldwide. The articles are well-edited and always contain the pertinent contact details for any trip.

This is one of the best travel sites on the web, as it's concise, readable, frank, extensive, and somehow personal. It's useful for all, regardless of gender.

OTHER SITES OF INTEREST

Rainbow Adventures
www.rainbowadventures.com (see p. 82)

Bargain and Discount Travel

There must be something in the British constitution, which states that there is nothing more satisfying than getting good value for money. For those of you who are nodding your head in agreement and need to plan some type of travel, whether it be a flight or an entire holiday, the following sites have a lot to offer.

www.bargainholidays.com
Bargainholidays

Overall rating: ★ ★ ★ ★ ★			
Classification:	E-agent	**Readability:**	★ ★ ★ ★ ★
Updating:	Regularly	**Content:**	★ ★ ★ ★ ★
Navigation:	★ ★ ★ ★ ★	**Speed:**	★ ★ ★ ★ ★

UK R

Bargainholidays specialises in late-availability holidays or flight-only deals from the UK. The homepage is clearly set out with the best last-minute deals listed centrally and a lot of holiday sun choices, especially suited for booking on those grey British days when a computer screen provides the only light. One can choose a budget limit and proceed, or look for what is available this weekend or on special offer. Car hire is also available. All details are listed on the site, but bookings are by phone.

SPECIAL FEATURES

This Weekend is a simple list of the hundreds of weekend or short breaks available at short notice, sorted by city and price. Many of the trips provide a cheaper alternative to staying at home for the weekend, which makes them very enticing.

Find a Holiday gives the choice of searching by destination, date, or sun holiday. The enquiries are speedily answered and new searches are easy to start up.

This site should definitely be bookmarked for all last minute holidays from the UK.

www.deckchair.com
Deckchair

Overall rating: ★ ★ ★ ★			
Classification:	E-agent	**Readability:**	★ ★ ★ ★ ★
Updating:	Regularly	**Content:**	★ ★ ★ ★ ★
Navigation:	★ ★ ★ ★ ★	**Speed:**	★ ★ ★ ★ ★

UK R

This really is the most super-efficient online booker on the internet. Founded by Bob Geldof and James Page, it has a no-nonsense homepage, which lists a few of the best fares available, and a short registration that leads to the flight search and booking.

What makes this site so ticket-buyer-friendly is that it immediately shows on one single page using one click, the airline, availability, schedule, and price for each flight that fits the chosen destination and dates. This allows a search with no endless trying for various alternatives; all the information is there. Hooray! The site has also recently added accommodation and car hire booking to its services.

SPECIAL FEATURES

Ask the World leads to a globe-headed helper who will answer any travel question, and links to tourism sites, restaurant guides, and other relevant information worldwide.

Flights is a search facility, which asks you when you want to fly and where you want to fly from and to. It then searches for a list of available flights from various airlines, though the process can be very slow.

Ask Car Hire Another simple search facility, which helps you locate car-hire companies around the globe. Either a name, address and contact number is listed, or you can follow a link straight through to the relevant site.

Ask Hotels connects you to hotel directories and tourist information websites, as well as individual hotels.

A superior, super-fast, and super-clear online booker for flights, accommodation, and car-hire.

Luxury Travel

Take heed. Don't visit the following sites unless you are intent on depleting your bank account. On the other hand, these sites present helpful information for those who feel they want some luxury and deserve it. It may be a once in a lifetime experience so use the websites to make sure you do it right.

www.headwater.com
Headwater

Overall rating: ★ ★ ★ ★

Classification:	Tour Operator	**Readability:**	★ ★ ★ ★ ★
Updating:	Regularly	**Content:**	★ ★ ★ ★ ★
Navigation:	★ ★ ★	**Speed:**	★ ★ ★

UK R

This UK-based luxury tour operator has a rather over-discreet homepage, which would benefit from the addition of some company information, but some truly amazing holidays can be found by clicking on the sun and snow choices. In these separate sites, the holidays are fully detailed, with some being custom-made, others for organised groups, and still more for the independent type. A lot of care has gone into introducing the destinations and the activities (cycling, hiking, canoeing, or cross-country-skiing, to name just a few). The holidays look wonderful, the customer seems well-cared for, there's good eating and the benefit of considerable local knowledge. They are clearly outlined, but of course, these are the type of holidays which require further discussion, so booking is by phone.

SPECIAL FEATURES

Destinations can be found by clicking on Sun, and gives an idea of the individuality and allure of Headwater's holidays, such as secret Provence cycling, following the trail of Napoleon, Alsace wine trail hike, Venetian villas cycling and walking in reindeer country.

A site for extremely unusual and high quality walking, cycling, skiing and canoeing holidays.

www.luxurylink.com
Luxury Link

Overall rating: ★ ★ ★ ★ ★			
Classification: Database		**Readability:**	★ ★ ★ ★ ★
Updating: Regularly		**Content:**	★ ★ ★ ★ ★
Navigation: ★ ★ ★ ★ ★		**Speed:**	★ ★ ★ ★ ★

US

Targeted at those who have full diaries and like to book in advance, Luxury Link present an impressive collection of luxury holidays, resorts, intimate getaways, recommendations, auctions, and travel news, in a well-designed newsletter format. The site generally operates with small pictures and descriptions (all very positive, a bit womens' magazine-like) which link to the service's official site. Some really high-flying options are available such as flying around the world by private jet, travelling in a Turkish balloon, yacht adventures with nightly palace stops, or private tours of French wineries. There are many others to choose from in this well-solicited and very well-presented database. Every aspect of browsing this site is pleasurable but the visuals are particularly good, which can be oh, so important when trying to picture a holiday. The posh auction site even lists past auction results.

SPECIAL FEATURES

Tour Calendar is a real gift for holiday planning, as it lists holidays by week, so preferred seasons and special events are captured at a glance.

Travel Research is a super link to luxury magazines and all practical travel information sites.

An elegant and information-packed site, for those planning or dreaming of luxury travel.

www.simply-travel.com
Simply Travel

Overall rating: ★ ★ ★ ★ ★			
Classification: Tour Operator		**Readability:**	★ ★ ★ ★ ★
Updating: Regularly		**Content:**	★ ★ ★ ★ ★
Navigation: ★ ★ ★ ★ ★		**Speed:**	★ ★ ★ ★ ★

UK R

Simply Travel offers online and telephone booking from its attractive and quickly navigable site, which offers a huge range for the discerning traveller. It gives discounts for online booking, a list of late savers, and an amazing geographical choice. Simply Travel offers holidays in Greece, Tuscany, Spain, Portugal, Italy, Corsica, Turkey, and Crete, and has special winter sun and city or short break destinations. It's a refreshing site that more than fulfils its name.

SPECIAL FEATURES

Simply Cities and Short Breaks provides a good introduction to the full range and quality of the holidays on offer: Budapest, Bermuda, Marrakech, Paris, Vienna, Bilbao...this page also enables pre-booking of concert tickets, bottles of champagne, and flowers, as well as a list of cultural highlights for each city.

A big choice of upmarket, personal holidays combined with a well-functioning site.

For other ideas on luxury travel see Boutique and Luxury Hotels on p. 79 and tour operators on p. 53.

Gay and Lesbian Travel

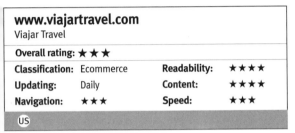

www.viajartravel.com
Viajar Travel

Overall rating: ★ ★ ★			
Classification: Ecommerce		**Readability:**	★ ★ ★ ★
Updating: Daily		**Content:**	★ ★ ★ ★
Navigation: ★ ★ ★		**Speed:**	★ ★ ★

US

Viajar travel is a global gay and lesbian web travel guide, and this site, which is sponsored by the guide, offers first-hand reports from travellers and advice on many aspects of gay and lesbian travel.

SPECIAL FEATURES

Viajar Advice Forum is a message board where you can post a query, or add your comments in response to a question.

Features consists, at the moment, of a single article on the policies of various resorts towards gay and lesbian couples.

Travelogues contains traveller's own detailed accounts of their voyages. It is mainly focused on travelling in the USA, with a few pieces focussing on the rest of the world.

News promises up-to-date travel news, advisories and alerts for the gay traveller, though, it looked like items are not added on a regular basis.

Well-designed site, which has the potential to grow into a healthy travel resource.

OTHER SITES OF INTEREST

Freedom Travel UK
www.freedomtraveluk.com/yellow.htm

Amigos London
www.amigos-london.co.uk

Damron
www.damron.com

Planet Out
www.planetout.com/pno/travel

Out and About Online
www.outandabout.com

Gay Explorer
www.gayexplorer.com

Chapter 5

finance and documentation

'When I have to read economic documents I have to have a box of matches and start moving them into position to simplify and illustrate the points to myself.'

From the Observer, 16 September 1962

'Got the passport, got some dosh' is what commonly runs through the mind as you dash for the airport. Without the correct documentation and some resources to rely on, travelling can be a sticky business.

Beyond that, there are other decisions to be made, such as what type of insurance is required. The following sites help to organise all the administrative details before taking off.

Travel Insurance

As with any financial agreement, the words of advice here are 'read the small print'. The following sites sell travel insurance online, which is convenient, but the policies differ greatly. Until there is an online travel insurance broker the prices will vary dramatically as well. The market is changing swiftly though, and these discrepancies should be smoothed out in the near future.

www.travel-bug.co.uk
Flynow

Overall rating: ★★★★★			
Classification:	Insurance	**Readability:**	★★★★★
Updating:	Regular	**Content:**	★★★★★
Navigation:	★★★★	**Speed:**	★★★★★

UK

To access this super-quick, super-cheap insurance service, which is available to UK residents only, click on Travel Insurance from the left-hand menu bar and take advantage of the Pricing Wizard's magic. Using the Pricing Wizard is a one-step process yielding instantaneous and very reasonably priced quotes, with all details immediately available. It's a real breeze to complete as almost no information regarding birth dates or schooling is required.

Flynow uses the specialist travel insurance brokers Campbell Irvine Ltd, with underwriters from Lloyds, to arrange these travel insurance schemes. The policies seem to be very good value, and include hourly travel delay payments, a good number of ski and scuba days, and very good sports coverage. It is extremely helpful to have the terms and conditions of the policy on the main travel insurance page. There are many options for customising policies, but in many cases the best choice is an annual policy.

An almost instant response on a hassle-free site giving great travel insurance.

www.screentrade.co.uk
Screentrade

Overall rating: ★ ★ ★ ★ ★			
Classification:	Insurance	**Readability:**	★ ★ ★
Updating:	Regular	**Content:**	★ ★ ★ ★ ★
Navigation:	★ ★ ★	**Speed:**	★ ★ ★ ★ ★

UK

This very competitive insurance site is useful, convenient, and certainly money-saving. Screentrade makes big promises about competitive prices and offers to pay the difference if lower prices are found.

From the homepage, click on the type of insurance needed to go immediately to the personal details and requirements form. The user is presented with the full details (insurer, policy components, duration) of all proposed policies within seconds of making a request.

Policies can be purchased immediately online, and are issued by several major UK insurance companies. The buyer makes the final choice as to which policy to purchase. The whole process only takes a few minutes, even though the questionnaire is more cumbersome than some other insurance sites, asking for birth date and schooling status. Only one filling-in session is required, however, as personal details can be easily retrieved for future requests or an interest in another type of policy.

A very competitive and easy-to-operate UK site for online purchase of travel insurance, and including motor and home as well.

www.travelinsurers.com
TIA

Overall rating: ★ ★ ★ ★ ★			
Classification:	Insurance	**Readability:**	★ ★ ★ ★ ★
Updating:	Regular	**Content:**	★ ★ ★ ★ ★
Navigation:	★ ★ ★ ★ ★	**Speed:**	★ ★ ★ ★ ★

UK

TIA gives up trendy graphics for strong advice and a clear product summary. At last, a site that doesn't make buying a serious financial product feel as though one is playing with the children's computer game, although the homepage is a little wordy. The most amazing aspect of the TIA site is that it quotes policy prices immediately, without any further input from the buyer, and the prices are very competitive. A consortium of major, well-known UK insurers underwrite the policies.

TIA has seven categories to choose from: Single trip, Already away/Travelling from other countries, Annual multi-trip, Explorer (for the budget traveller), Policy coverage & territorial limits, Useful links, and Online ordering. Each area gives immediate quotes, and policies can be bought on the spot, with email confirmation and policy certificates by mail.

TIA offers a fourteen-day money-back warranty, and can provide cover for British travellers who have already begun their journey. TIA cannot give cover to US citizens, but those with dual US and UK citizenship can take advantage of the loophole.

Highly competitive and simple-to-use UK travel insurance site which appears, at the time of review, to offer the largest scope.

Cash and other Options

Travelling is much easier when you have the security of knowing you can obtain funds in an emergency situation, or check exchange rates when making an expensive purchase. The following sites help you to organise your spending money before you go, but also provide information on where to go should the need arise whilst away.

www.mastercard.com/atm
Mastercard International Cardholder Services

Overall rating: ★ ★ ★ ★

Classification:	ATM Locator	**Readability:**	★ ★ ★ ★ ★
Updating:	Regular	**Content:**	★ ★ ★ ★ ★
Navigation:	★ ★ ★ ★ ★	**Speed:**	★ ★ ★ ★ ★

US

MasterCard International has set up this site to inform travellers of the whereabouts of MasterCard Automatic Teller Machines (ATM) all over the world. The site also has sections on the many uses of the card, such as acquiring travellers cheques, and lists the services that merchants are obliged to provide when they accept MasterCard.

SPECIAL FEATURES

North American Locator swiftly locates every US MasterCard ATM. Entering the zip code, whilst not essential, makes the search go slightly faster. This facility answers requests with brightly coloured, clearly marked maps for machines and addresses. It's also a good way to get a map of US destinations.

Worldwide ATM Locator is not quite as swift as the US searcher, but it can find any ATM in anywhere in the world. Unfortunately, one can't input by specific locale, so time is spent scrolling through a menu of countries, but the information is all there.

A good site to visit, especially for more remote destinations where special plans have to be made to get cash.

www.oanda.com/converter/travel
OANDA

Overall rating: ★ ★ ★ ★ ★			
Classification: Exchange Rates		**Readability:**	★ ★ ★ ★ ★
Updating: Regular		**Content:**	★ ★ ★ ★ ★
Navigation:	★ ★ ★ ★ ★	**Speed:**	★ ★ ★ ★ ★

US

www.visa.com/pd/atm/
Visa

Overall rating: ★ ★ ★ ★ ★			
Classification: ATM Locator		**Readability:**	★ ★ ★ ★ ★
Updating: Regular		**Content:**	★ ★ ★ ★ ★
Navigation:	★ ★ ★ ★ ★	**Speed:**	★ ★ ★ ★ ★

US

Many of the online travel agents offer their own currency conversion features, but OANDA's traveller currency cheat sheet makes the visitor feel like a professional currency trader-in-training. It's very easy to use, even by the most numerically illiterate.

The best money-saving feature is the choice of rates: unlike bureaux de change, you can choose to view the official, typical credit card, or typical cash rate.

SPECIAL FEATURES

Get my Cheat Sheet brings up a neat chart listing the exchange rate between your chosen currencies of values between £1 to £5,000.

Reverse Cheat Sheet reveals the same conversions the opposite way round, with the foreign currency first. These can be printed out and popped in a wallet, meaning that shop-a-holics no longer have any excuse for making mistakes in how much things cost.

A worthwhile stop for exchange rates before any trip.

Visa's site is useful for finding ATMs and serves as a reminder of the services that Visa offers. The ATM locators are speedy and fun to use, and produce very useful destination maps for the most far-flung or over-urbanised destinations. There are also explanations of the latest Visa products for travellers.

SPECIAL FEATURES

Consumer Tips is a wonderful pre-travel briefing section. It explains the Euro, and has travel safety recommendations and card user information. The best link on this page is to the matching game found under Travel Resources, which is a fun international culture and etiquette quiz. Print it out and use it as an after-dinner party game!

Travel Resources lists all the Visa Travel financial products and services, travel tips, and gives very comprehensive links to embassies, consulates, travel guides, language and currency sites, time zones, measurement converters and more.

For all travellers with a Visa card, this super-speedy ATM locator is full of information and gives fantastically useful links to other travel-related sites.

Passport and Visas

Travelling abroad requires a passport. The following site means no longer having to stand in queues at the passport office, and questions about visas can be asked via email. This site is also helpful for anyone with foreign friends or employees that may have questions about their status in the United Kingdom.

www.ukpa.gov.uk/ukpass.htm
British Passport Office

Overall rating: ★★★★★

Classification:	Government	Readability:	★★★★★
Updating:	Occasionally	Reliability:	★★★★★
Navigation:	★★★★★	Speed:	★★★★

UK

Avoid the all-day queue just to ask a question about renewing a passport or visa requirement. You can apply for the necessary application forms on this red, white, and blue site, which is super-easy to navigate and a far superior way to spend one's time.

SPECIAL FEATURES

Travel Advice gives information on visas for travellers entering the UK.

Applications and Renewals guides you through the process of first-tme applications, passports for babies and children and what to do if you need to amend your passport or it gets lost or stolen.

How to Apply lists basic details on how to fill in the forms, and where to send them.

Urgent Applications details the procedures to follow if you need a passport within 48 hrs or two weeks.

UKPA Regional Offices Locations, maps and opening times of the UKPAs regional offices.

UKPA High Street Partners is a search facility, which will locate the nearest passport agent to your home. For a small administration fee, agents (which include many post office branches) will forward your application to the relevant passport office.

Enquiries allows you to track the process of passport or other applications, or ask questions by email of a Passport Office official.

Rules and Eligibility tells you who can apply and where to do it.

Most definitely bookmark this site — it's the way to go for dealing with UK passport issues.

OTHER SITES OF INTEREST

Foreign and Commonwealth Office
www.fco.gov.uk/links.asp
This is a directory of links to the official websites of British Government interests abroad. For information on travelling in a specific country, use this site to source the region's British Embassy, High Commission, or Consulate.

Lonely Planet
www.lonelyplanet.com
Look under the country you're travelling to for full details of visa requirements.

Embassy Web.com
www.embpage.org
Search for the contact details of virtually every embassy in the world.

Chapter 6

further travel resources

'Now, what I want is, Facts... Facts alone are wanted in life.'

Charles Dickens (1854)

After the flight is booked and the hotel has been reserved, to make the most out of a holiday or business trip you need to be prepared. The number of websites offering help in this area is enormous, far too many to even hope to comprehensively assess. Here though, are listed some of the most interesting and useful sites to help make sure travelling is everything it can and should be...from safe to exciting and adventurous!

Packing Tips

Many men wonder why women can't travel lightly. These men should ask their lady friends to visit the following sites. They are aimed at anybody who tends to pack too much, or would like tips on how to arrive and unpack without finding creased shirts and leaking tubes of toothpaste, and are interesting to many more than overzealous female packers.

www.packinglight.com
Packing Light

Overall rating: ★ ★ ★ ★			
Classification:	Information	**Readability:**	★ ★ ★ ★
Updating:	Weekly	**Content:**	★ ★ ★
Navigation:	★ ★ ★ ★	**Speed:**	★ ★ ★ ★

US

Learn how to pack a 22-inch carry-on bag for easy, carefree travel on this creative site. Sponsored by Halloway Travel Outfitters, the site gives a long list of products for packing light, including everything from gadgets to disposable briefs. It also offers a six-step method for packing light complete with bundling techniques and regulations for zipping and buttoning every item. Illustrations guide the first-time packer through a precise process of folding a garment into the suitcase. Included are answers to questions such as how to pack lightly for a two-climate trip. Don't forget that this is a promotional site and most of the products mentioned are carried by the sponsor in California.

SPECIAL FEATURES

Currency Conversion converts from any currency into another to help plan how much money is needed for a trip.

Services generates a long list of travel videos currently on the market.

Checklists gives a list of documents to take, things to do to your home before leaving for a trip (stop the post, turn down the thermostat), and of course the ultimate checklist for packing.

Good practical advice and helpful illustrations on helping one prepare and pack for a trip.

www.oratory.com/travel
The Compleat Carry-on Traveler

Overall rating: ★ ★ ★ ★

Classification:	Information	Readability:	★ ★ ★ ★
Updating:	Weekly	Content:	★ ★ ★ ★
Navigation:	★ ★ ★ ★	Speed:	★ ★ ★ ★

US

Resources is a directory of recommended products and books with information on where to find them.

Mailing List keeps subscribers up to date with late-breaking news on travel luggage sales.

Perfect for the over-packer who needs to lighten up, and excellent for the frequent traveller looking for concrete tips on how less really is more.

A site that gives tips on travelling light, founded by Doug Dyment, a frequent traveller who after years of lugging learned that by lightening the burden he enjoyed travelling much more. Dyment offers packing techniques, products, and advice on how to live for an indefinite period of time out of just one carry-on bag. According to Dyment, travellers can save money by carrying just one bag safely by their side, as there is then no need to tip porters, take a taxi, or worry about theft. In addition, one has greater freedom to change travel plans, since a carry-on bag need not be checked. Everyone who's ever bemoaned a partner's over-packing will love this site.

SPECIAL FEATURES

What To Take is a one-page packing check-list for travelling with one bag. It offers advice on choosing clothing, doing laundry, packing toiletries, and selecting luggage.

What To Take It In offers dimensions, prices, construction advice (soft or hard), and a list of carry-on limits for a variety of airlines.

How To Pack It describes techniques on how to fit everything into one bag, including soap powder, hangers, and spot remover for doing laundry.

Sponsored by the Snow Sports Industries of America, this site provides a comprehensive list of what to pack for a ski vacation. It's very thorough, and one wonders if people really need to be reminded to pack after-ski shoes or a credit card. Some items are a useful reminder, though, such as heat packs to stick in gloves and boots, and a portable boot dryer, no less. Not knowing these handy items existed is no excuse, for apparently you can't ski without them. It's also interesting to learn that cotton socks or undergarments should never be packed for skiing. The site suggests sleeping in your long underwear but most people would surely want to change out of them after a hard day's skiing. Some items are listed as an enticement to follow links to an equipment, clothing, and accessory company, and on the whole the site is best used for shopping rather than packing. It also offers links to lots of American ski information.

SPECIAL FEATURES

Ski/Snowboard vacation packing checklist is a list that could be printed out and customised according to your own requirements. Basically it's a ski vacation packing list to take through life.

A great site for those going on their first time ski holiday and aren't sure what to take besides those long things to put on your feet!

Restaurants and Entertainment

For many people a good night out with a great meal is the point of travel. If you want to make sure of getting a table at a sought-after restaurant, or tickets to a gala concert, use these sites to plan your evenings in advance.

www.fodors.com/reviews/drevselect.cfm
Fodors Guides

Overall rating: ★ ★ ★ ★ ★			
Classification:	Restaurant	Readability:	★ ★ ★ ★
Updating:	Regularly	Content:	★ ★ ★ ★ ★
Navigation:	★ ★ ★ ★ ★	Speed:	★ ★ ★ ★

UK

Of all the online restaurant guides, Fodor's gives the most comprehensive international coverage. The URL given above takes you straight to the dining reviews, but there are other useful features at the fodors.com homepage, such as lodging reviews, smart travel tips, and create your own miniguides to your destination. Use the Site Shortcuts pull-down menu from any page to find the full range of services.

For restaurants, you can choose to search by name from a complete listing for your destination, or narrow down the selection by price, facilities or location. Having chosen your preferred search method, select your destination from Europe, United States and Canada, Africa and the Middle East, The Caribbean and the Atlantic, Latin America, and Asia, Australia and the Pacific. Roll your curser over one of these categories and a full list of the destinations covered in that region appears.

The reviews themselves are accurate rather than colourful, but the Fodor's Choice, marked with red asterisks, seem well chosen and independent.

Maps of the areas are provided, although individual restaurant locations are not highlighted.

Certainly the first choice for far-flung foodies, though competes less well on the beaten track.

OTHER SITES OF INTEREST

Zagat's
www.zagat.com
Hugely popular American restaurant guides in which readers readers rate each venue. Now covers London, Paris, Tokyo, Toronto and Vancouver as well as providing comprehensive coverage of the US.

Hardens
www.hardens.com
The editor's choice for UK dining.

Time Out
www.timeout.com
Lively reviews of restaurants, arts and entertainment in 31 cities (see p. 17).

Ticketmaster
www.ticketmaster.com and **www.ticketmaster.co.uk**
Online booking for sports, arts and entertainment events.

Omniticket
www.omniticket.com
Entertainment ticketing and distribution. Only Paris was live at the time of review but Italy, Australia, Korea and the US are promised.

Maps and Locators

The time has come that we no longer have to wrestle with huge pieces of paper which have torn in the fold creases or lug heavy books around with us whilst travelling. The following websites allow us to print off either one page district maps, or specific route directions in writing — with a diagram to relieve us of all the extra baggage.

www.RAC.co.uk
RAC

Overall rating: ★ ★ ★ ★

Classification:	Information	**Readability:**	★ ★ ★
Updating:	Fortnightly	**Content:**	★ ★ ★ ★ ★
Navigation:	★ ★ ★ ★	**Speed:**	★ ★ ★ ★

UK

This site is designed to be user-friendly and offers many free services, including a useful route planner, a hotel-finder, live traffic news, and servicing tips so you won't have to spend money at the garage. But should you find yourself with a leaky carburettor or broken hub cap, this site also gives you a list of questions to ask your garage so as not to be overcharged. Designed in an array of bold colors with the respected RAC logo discreetly in the corner, this is a site where it's best to use the map to get around. If your question is about cars, this site will have the answer.

SPECIAL FEATURES

Route Planner is the most useful feature on the site and covers any driving trip in the UK or Europe. Just type in a departure town and a destination point and it will churn out detailed directions. One can even name three towns for stops to see friends along the way and it will plan your journey accordingly.

Car Advice offers simple tips for keeping one's car in good nick, and anyone with any questions regarding UK motoring laws, insurance, or driver's licences should look here. The RAC gives a helpful checklist of questions to ask before signing a motor insurance policy, and lists second-hand car dealers whose vehicles have been inspected and protected by RAC engineers. These cars have apparently been put through more than seventy inspections and investigations.

Also available in this section is a list of safe travel tips including avoiding a breakdown and first aid advice.

Buy Online covers maps, guides, and books, as well as an array of motoring accessories such as a first aid kit, fire extinguisher, and emergency motoring kit. You can also buy different levels of European Motoring Assistance to cover your vehicle when you are outside the country, as well as insurance to cover legal expenses.

Your voice is where you can share your views with other angry motorists about the price of petrol, speed limits, or traffic. Start a new topic if you like; it's a healthy, constructive way to handle road rage.

The UK's most respected automobile club command respect and trust on this site.

www.map-guides.com
map-guides

Overall rating: ★ ★ ★ ★ ★			
Classification: Bookshop		**Readability:**	★ ★ ★
Updating: Daily		**Content:**	★ ★ ★ ★
Navigation: ★ ★ ★ ★		**Speed:**	★ ★ ★ ★

UK

This multi-faceted site, hosted by the Traveller's World bookshop, allows one to browse and buy maps and travel guides for at least ten per cent off the normal retail price. Their stock seems to cover every crevice of the world. Features include a book and map of the month for a specific region, providing enthusiasm and incentive for planning a trip to that location. Specific maps for motor touring, cycling, and climbing in the area of the month, which at the time of review was France, are also listed, together with locations of UK retail outlets where they can be bought. The site is quite easy to use: simply select your destination and wait for a long list of products to appear. The only problem is that the books aren't reviewed, so it can be hard to know which to choose. The maps, luckily, are broken down by area, otherwise you would be really lost. Orders should arrive within seven days, and all products are refundable within 14 days.

SPECIAL FEATURES

Advanced Search allows you to search for a book or map by the publisher's name, type of product, or title if you know it.

Guide to Map Scales gives a brief lesson in cartography that is meant to be simple but could confuse the novice.

Latest Offers supposedly gives information on their special discounts. However, when we visited the only information present stated that all books and maps are discounted, which is already apparent elsewhere in the site.

This site is a fast way to find nearly all the published titles covering specific travel destinations, and is an easy way to find the map of your choice.

www.mapquest.com
Mapquest

Overall rating: ★ ★ ★			
Classification:	Online Maps	**Readability:**	★ ★ ★
Updating:	Daily	**Content:**	★ ★ ★ ★
Navigation:	★ ★	**Speed:**	★ ★ ★

US

This site offers a door-to-door driving map service for the United States, Canada, and Mexico. Simply type in a starting point and destination and, miraculously, detailed directions pop up on how to get there. It also tells you how long your trip is likely to take, and the total distance of your journey. Travellers can ask for information on any traffic incidents along the way, popular attractions to visit en route, and even look up business addresses and telephone numbers, which appear to cover most cities in the US.

Despite all these good things, the yellow and white pages, jumbled graphics, photos and flashing adverts can leave you feeling quite dizzy, and the site can be cumbersome and difficult to navigate.

SPECIAL FEATURES

City Guide Unfortunately, the site often tries to cover too much, and this guide is a prime example. It offers news, weather, entertainment, shopping, and dining information for all major US cities, but also posts photos of missing children broken down by area, and offers a personal dating service for finding someone geographically desirable.

Business Traveler offers a hotel search for anywhere in the world, gives airport terminal maps and driving directions, with printable online maps.

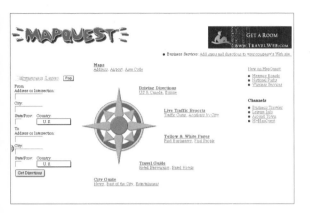

Leisure provides maps of National Parks, scenic drives, and a more personal map service for planning a trip.

Around Town offers help if you intend to move to the US, with services to help calculate a salary based on the cost of living index in your new town, and a list of more than 12,000 reports on public school districts and child care centres.

My Mapquest lets you save all your map and address requests and provides you with a password to access your information at a later date.

An interesting site, but stick to the basics: the driving direction service, hotel search, and restaurant guide. Beyond that, one could suffer website motion sickness.

OTHER SITES OF INTEREST

Michelin Travel Route Planner - Europe
www.michelin-travel.com/eng/itin/demande/vide.cgi

CW Lease
www.cwlease.com/cwlint/index2.htm

euroShell - route planner
www.euroshell.com/int/en/index.asp

Drive Alive
www.drive-alive.com

Weather Reports

Don't know what to pack for that weekend away on the continent? Use the following sites to see if the brolly is needed to fend off April showers, or if a bikini and suntan lotion would be more appropriate.

Find out detailed information about the weather anywhere in the world on this very comprehensive site. It's part of the BBC Online service and includes many different features in a fun and easy-to-read package. Serious weather warnings are given when necessary, gardeners will love the monthly gardening advice column on what can be planted when, and there's plenty of environmental information.

SPECIAL FEATURES

Five-day Forecast gives a city-by-city five-day forecast whether one is driving to Doncaster or jetting to Jamaica. Choose a continent then the nearest city from the drop-down menus and enough information is given to help a traveller pack appropriately for nearly a week.

Holiday Weather around the world includes several different features. There's information on the European Sun Index and keeping safe in the sun, and each week a popular holiday destination is targeted and detailed geographical and meteorological information for the area is given.

Satellite and Radar Images allows a check of radar pictures of the US and UK, updated every three hours and showing, through color coding, where there is rain.

Producing the Weather keeps the weather junkie happy by giving all the facts and history on the BBC Weather Centre in London, including photographs and biographies of the eighteen meteorologists.

The Year so Far lets anyone with lots of time on their hands compare this year's temperature, rainfall and sunshine with the averages for previous years. How can anyone scientifically predict weather when it varies so greatly...?

Inshore Waters Forecast may help with planning an afternoon sail since it gives information on visibility, storms, and wind direction.

This site offers reliable ways to plan a safe trip by car, boat, or plane. It would also suit the weather-obsessed as well those who want to check the latest pressure centres around the world.

www.csac.org
Cyberspace Avalanche Center

Overall rating: ★ ★ ★ ★ ★

Classification:	Information	**Readability:**	★ ★ ★ ★
Updating:	Daily	**Content:**	★ ★ ★ ★ ★
Navigation:	★ ★ ★ ★	**Speed:**	★ ★ ★ ★

US R

This easy-to-use, well-laid-out site is the best on offer for anyone who skis or climbs. Get updated information on the latest mountain conditions in Europe, Canada, and the United States, and receive warnings, forecast discussions, hourly reports, and climate data sent in from local avalanche and forestry service officials. Compiled by the Snow and Avalanche Center, a US-based non-profit organisation, the site is written by experts and offers many cautionary tales whilst still encouraging sport fanatics to get out there and tackle the mountain. So, if your ambition is to climb every mountain, first hike through this informational site. It should lead to a safer, more pleasant, journey.

SPECIAL FEATURES

Educational Resources offers a multiple choice safety quiz, articles on skill and safety while skiing, climbing, snow boarding, and snow mobiling as well as tips on identifying dangerous conditions and advice on how to handle an avalanche if you are unlucky enough to get caught in one.

Other Cool Stuff presents photos of avalanches in motion and archives on avalanche movies. Yikes!

Store sells transceivers, shovels, probes, books, videos, and a whole lot of other mountain paraphernalia, all to buy online.

Map Directory links to avalanche information centres around the world.

Incident Reports keeps statistics and reports on all fatalities in North America and most in Europe.

Bulletin Archives lists the history of weather conditions in selected areas.

A great site for the serious mountaineer who likes to ski dangerously in safety.

www.meto.gov.uk
Meteorological Office

Overall rating: ★ ★ ★			
Classification:	Information	**Readability:**	★★★
Updating:	Every 6 Hours	**Content:**	★★★★★
Navigation:	★★★★	**Speed:**	★★★★

UK

Provided by the British Government Meteorological Office, this site provides a five-day forecast for anywhere in the world indexed by city, continent, or region. Meteorologists out there will no doubt find the latest infra-red satellite pictures, updated every six hours, greatly interesting, but a little more information for the casual observer would be welcome. One can also access pressure charts but that's also quite tricky for the novice - a bit like cumulus clouds!

SPECIAL FEATURES

World Weather News has cute titles like 'melting mounties', 'drippy Dieppe' and 'Portugese plonk' which tell about warm weather in Canada, and rain in Belgium and Portugal.

Education gives a list of even more sites to find information about weather, just in case this wasn't enough. Learn about weather measurements, tropical cyclones, and automatic weather stations.

Services offers a weather hotline to the general public by phone or fax, as well as detailed marine, mountain, and aviation forecasts by fax. This page also offers a tailored weather service to businesses.

Search can be made by typing in any weather information, query, or concept.

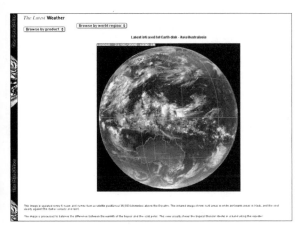

This site offers no-nonsense, completely straightforward weather news. Other sites offer the same information in a more interesting context, but for weather nerds or meteorologists-in-training, it's seventh heaven.

OTHER SITES OF INTEREST

Weather.com
www.weather.com/intl
Detailed information and temperatures given in Fahrenheit

Travel Notes
www.travelnotes.org/weather/index.htm

Travel Related Shopping

The following sites offer the chance to buy luggage, sports equipment or duty free, to those travelling, or even those staying at home. This form of shopping can work very well, but make sure you read the return policies in the event that the product isn't what you expected.

Any skier knows how frustrating it can be to lose half a day's skiing while waiting to rent equipment for the family on the first day of the holiday. This bilingual site allows skiers to rent and reserve Alpine, Nordic, and snowboard equipment online for more than 150 French ski resorts so that they can be the first on the slopes on the day of arrival.

The site has fun graphics, which can inspire you to plan a ski vacation just to rent the skis - even if you already have a pair. Oh, and the photos of tanned skiers tackling fresh powder under blue skies makes one forget just how cold and grey it can be on the slopes in February.

From the Homepage, click Go In to enter the secure online renting facility. You are then guided through a three step process, which allows you to book your equipment.

SPECIAL FEATURES

Book Your Skis Online Just type in the resort, choose from a list of stores in the area, and then decide which type of skis are required based on level of expertise, height, weight, and , shoe size. A week's rental for an adult can cost less than £70, with a choice of £40 brands of skis including Salomon, Dynastar, and Rossignol. The only hassle could be getting to the store to pick them up: for the visitor unfamiliar with the area, finding the skis could be the real challenge.

Our Assembly Specialists give tips from the masters in boot fitting and ski equipment on how to get the best boot, and choose the right equipment, for both ski-ing and mountaineering.

A handy, time-saving site that will take the stress out of the first day of a ski vacation by allowing skiers to hit the slopes instead of the rental shop.

www.baa.co.uk
BAA

Overall rating: ★ ★ ★ ★			
Classification:	Information	**Readability:**	★ ★ ★ ★
Updating:	Monthly	**Content:**	★ ★ ★ ★
Navigation:	★ ★ ★	**Speed:**	★ ★ ★ ★

UK

Operated by BAA, the well-known managing company of Heathrow and 14 other airports, this site provides a list of stores located in their UK airports and offers a special shopping collection service at Heathrow allowing one to buy more and carry less. Site users must be travelling from the UK to a destination in the European Union to use this service which enables them to buy from as many stores as they want (except for liquor and tobacco) and collect the goods upon return at the International Arrivals Hall.

SPECIAL FEATURES

Online Shopping is great should you be dashing past Austin Reed at the airport with no time to buy that tie for hubby: buy it here later. Every store in Heathrow Airport, from the Caviar House to Chinacraft is accessible from here.

Online Travel offers links to www.lastminute.com (see p.45) for flight deals, www.hertz.co.uk (see p.63) for rental cars, and www.expedia.co.uk (see p.44) for weekend breaks and holidays, making one question where the real focus lies.

For the passenger with a layover at Heathrow, planned or unplanned, this site is definitely worth checking out, and will help make the most of your time.

www.letravelstore.com
Le Travel Store

Overall rating: ★ ★ ★ ★			
Classification: Eretail		**Readability:**	★ ★ ★
Updating: Weekly		**Content:**	★ ★ ★ ★
Navigation: ★ ★ ★ ★		**Speed:**	★ ★ ★ ★

US

This family-run travel store from San Diego, California, offers travel gear, luggage, and accessories for world travellers. Featuring luggage by Eagle Creek Travel Gear, and books by the Rough Guide and Lonely Planet, this site has the effect of making you want to depart on an adventure trip immediately.

The site is very easy to navigate and offers lots of luggage products, from wheel-away bags to duffels, with large clear photos so you can tell what you're buying. International orders can be made by phone or email. Orders will be confirmed by email and anything sent overseas will be air-insured. Bear in mind that international buyers have to pick up both the tax and customs duty when items arrive from abroad.

To buy a particular item, click Add to Shopping Cart. This brings up a tally of your selected items and the subtotal, you've spent. From here you can either click Continue Shopping or Checkout, at which point you enter your address and delivery details.

SPECIAL FEATURES

Be There features travel diaries of staff members and friends, and at time of review followed one man around the world from Cambodia to Saigon, India, and Hong Kong.

Product Index is an online catalogue of all the products on offer at the site. These consist mainly of travel accessories, such as luggage, money belts and wallets, voltage converters and travel guides. Item listings are accompaniedby a brief description and small photograph.

A very lively online travel store with a personal touch. So much so that site visitors may find themselves tempted to pick up the phone and talk to the couple who own the store, after reading their riveting life story and viewing pictures of travel en famille.

www.samsonite-europe.com
Samsonite Europe

Overall rating: ★ ★ ★ ★			
Classification:	Ecommerce	Readability:	★ ★ ★ ★
Updating:	Rarely	Content:	★ ★ ★ ★
Navigation:	★ ★ ★ ★	Speed:	★ ★ ★ ★

US

Sponsored by the famous hundred-year-old luggage company of the same name, this is a lively site, even offering an online puzzle to identify the make and style of a mystery bag and win a free piece of luggage. Unfortunately, this takes place over a number of weeks, and if you can barely identify your own suitcases at the baggage claim, don't even attempt it. If you're uncertain what you want, browsing this site could take longer than driving to a shop and buying your luggage there. An online or postal catalogue is available, which may help with decision-making.

SPECIAL FEATURES

Hot Products Of The Month highlights new luggage series, with a special section on computer cases ranging from backpacks to briefcases and sleeves.

Find Your Favourite Travel Companion isn't as exciting as it sounds, but does allow one to browse for the ideal suitcase.

Product Catalogue allows you to choose the type of luggage you're after from drawings, further refine your choice, and then view photos of match-ups. The only problem is that it is sometimes difficult to tell if there are extra pockets or zippers from the photo. The travel gadget section is by far the most interesting since it offers everything from converters to locks, eye shades, umbrellas, and passport covers.

Travel Centre is a handy section that links to Samsonite's online travel magazine Focus On, and also offers links to transport, hotel, hostel, and villa rental sites. They also offer links to other sites for travel magazines and books.

For anyone who knows their luggage this is great. If not, it might take a while to make an educated choice, since they offer so many products in so many sizes and colours, all with different features. The downside of shopping for something like luggage on the internet is that you can't actually pick up the bag.

http://shop.baa.co.uk

shop@theairport. shop clever

Overall rating: ★ ★ ★			
Classification: Ecommerce		**Readability:**	★ ★ ★ ★
Updating: Daily		**Content:**	★ ★
Navigation: ★ ★ ★ ★		**Speed:**	★ ★

(UK)

This BAA-sponsored website should help travellers avoid the mad dash at the airport to find parking and change money. To use this site, you must be travelling abroad from BAA airports in southern England or Scotland. Select your airport and terminal from the drop-down menus, and proceed to the Currency, Shopping, or Parking services. This site still appears to have some glitches to work out: booking a parking spot and ordering a bottle of champagne both proved difficult, but when it works, it should be great.

SPECIAL FEATURES

Parking brings up a map of the parking structure for your chosen airport, but you can only pre-book up to 96 hours in advance.

Shopping offers a moving window of items from children's gifts to champagne. Duty free goods can also be pre-ordered here, with the exception of alcohol and tobacco if you're travelling within the European Union.

Currency offers up to seventy currencies, commission-free, at rates they claim match the bank.

Shopping Basket allows one to review the basket of items before entering the check out line.

This service could save time and stress at the airport before departure.

OTHER INTERESTED SITES

Windo Shop
www.windoshop.com

I want to shop
www.iwanttoshop.com

Mulberry
www.mulberry-england.co.uk/collections/luggage/

Travel Information, Health and Safety

Even if you've booked with the most accredited tour operator or travel agent, sometimes it is difficult to get the details you needs. The following sites help prepare travellers for every eventuality without having to make twenty telephone calls.

This site provides useful information for any traveller who has experienced the awful event of a hair dryer or razor exploding the moment it is plugged in at the hotel. Offering phone numbers around the world where people can recharge a modem, make a call on a cell phone, or adjust a VCR to fit a different international TV standard, it's a must for the frequent traveller. What else could one need? For the infrequent traveller who jets off to westernised cities this site may give more detailed information than is needed to make your electric toothbrush buzz. But for the far-flung business traveller, this could be a lifeline to communication in a distant town with an unpronounceable name. Ideal for expatriates planning to move a houseful of electrical equipment to a new country and wondering whether to bring the microwave or buy a new one there.

SPECIAL FEATURES

World Wide Phone Guide gives self-employed workers ideas on hooking-up a modem anywhere in the world.

World Electric Guide provides tips and information on electrical power around the globe.

International Dialing Codes lets you know how to make calls to and from most countries in the world.

Travel Photo Galleries gives an online peek of the website founder's extensive collection of scenic travel shots.

What's New gives new international dialling codes for East Timor and the Bahamas, plus television standard listings for Caicos, Uzbekistan and Latvia. Need new phone plug information for Croatia? It's here.

A very specific, well-informed website for anyone who has ever been frustrated by electricity issues when travelling. It allows you to decide which home comforts are worth packing.

www.fco.gov.uk/travel
Foreign and Commonwealth Office

Overall rating: ★ ★ ★			
Classification:	Information	**Readability:**	★ ★ ★ ★
Updating:	Frequently	**Content:**	★ ★ ★ ★ ★
Navigation:	★ ★ ★ ★	**Speed:**	★ ★ ★

UK

This is the official government site of the Foreign and Commonwealth Office, offering travel advice. A range of material is produced including advice on avoiding situations of political unrest, violence, natural disasters, epidemics, anti-British demonstrations, and information on aircraft safety. Using a drop-down menu, choose a country and a regularly updated page of travel advice will appear.

SPECIAL FEATURES

Do's and Don'ts allows users to click on a number of different countries and view the FCO cultural and practical

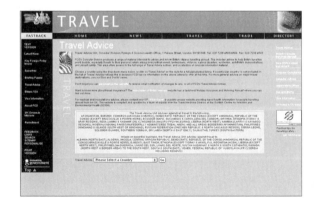

advice for that area as well as the addresses for British Embassies, Consulates, High Commissions, and Consular Offices. It's full of obscure practical information, for example, did you know that Cubans will not accept an American Express card, and that if travelling by train in Russia you should never accept drinks from rail staff in case you are drugged and your belongings stolen?

British Consular Services Abroad tells you what help can be provided by the British Consul overseas. It also provides a lengthy list of what the Consul cannot do like, provide better medical treatment than is given to local nationals.

Visa Information and Do I Need a UK Visa are pages directed at non-UK nationals visiting Britain rather than Brits going abroad.

A quirkily organised site, offering important and useful advice for travel to any country experiencing difficult circumstances.

www.airsafe.com
Airsafe

Overall rating: ★ ★ ★			
Classification:	Information	Readability:	★ ★ ★ ★
Updating:	Frequently	Content:	★ ★ ★ ★ ★
Navigation:	★ ★ ★ ★	Speed:	★ ★ ★

US

This site provides a list of the top ten airline safety tips. If you're afraid of flying, this site is not for you. The first safety tip is to avoid changing planes en route to your destination since 'most accidents occur during the take off, climb, descent, and the landing phase'. Comforting information! Other tips include paying attention to the pre-flight briefing and mentally noting the closest emergency exit, as well as not bringing hazardous material such as poisonous gases and corrosives on board the plane. The site also advises against wearing synthetic clothing while flying. Apparently, in the event of an evacuation on the escape slide, a polyester shirt might get 'hot due to friction, and melt causing first, second and third degree burns to the body and legs'. No thanks.

SPECIAL FEATURES

Child Safety offers up-to-date information on the newest air baby restraint called the Baby B'air which has been tested by the FAA and is designed to be worn by children under the age of two during the whole flight. Many mothers have been waiting for such an invention. You can order it online.

Fear of Flying makes even the most seasoned traveller worry after a quick look at the statistics on, amongst other things, airplane bombings. One can also contribute to their research by filling out the survey on degrees of fearfulness one feels in various plane situations or just link onto the phobia, panic and anxiety sites to learn more about the problem.

www.airlinesafety.com
Airline Safety

Overall rating: ★ ★ ★			
Classification:	Information	**Readability:**	★ ★ ★ ★
Updating:	Regularly	**Content:**	★ ★ ★ ★ ★
Navigation:	★ ★ ★ ★	**Speed:**	★ ★ ★

US

www.flyana.com
Healthy Flying

Overall rating: ★ ★ ★			
Classification:	Information	**Readability:**	★ ★ ★ ★
Updating:	Regularly	**Content:**	★ ★ ★ ★ ★
Navigation:	★ ★ ★ ★	**Speed:**	★ ★ ★

US

This site offers a variety of feature articles on airline safety but has a definite bias against government regulation of the industry. You can read editorials by pilots, explaining why the free market should be allowed to regulate flights. Other than this fairly obvious slant, the site makes for interesting reading, since it links to every book and article that has ever analysed flight safety, air crashes, or design faults in aircraft. The FAQ feature shows which seat is the safest on a plane, how to travel safely with an infant, and how common in-flight fires really are.

This site will helps one to feel well before, during, and after long haul or even short flights. Special features include a calendar for scheduling email reminders to update immunisations, booster shots and refill prescriptions, a travel first aid kit check-list, a healthy travel quiz, and a variety of articles and links to other health resources.

On-site feature articles include dealing with jet lag, health hazards while travelling, and neck pain from long haul flights. Some of this information can be really useful: 'Eight ways to protect your health while travelling' gives advice on everything from water safety to insect bites. And as most people tend not to think much about their health after arriving back home, this site explains when to worry about malaria, dysentery, or other serious illnesses that can be one of the drawbacks of exotic travel.

Finishing Touches

These sites are the ones which will help you put the finishing touches to your travel plans, and if that doesn't work and your meticulous plans go awry they'll give you advice on how to put things right.

www.atol.org.uk
Air Travel Organiser's Licence

Overall rating: ★ ★ ★			
Classification:	Information	Readability:	★ ★ ★
Updating:	Regularly	Content:	★ ★ ★
Navigation:	★ ★ ★	Speed:	★ ★ ★

UK

This site was founded to protect the public from losing their money, or being stranded abroad due to the collapse of an air travel firm. It aims to give comprehensive consumer protection to 27 million people in the UK who buy flights or air holidays each year. Through the site, visitors can check that a travel firm holds a licence to sell flights and package holidays by air. One can also use the site's Consumer Advice page and Helpline to handle any difficulties experienced with a tour operator. Through this site, which is managed by the Civil Aviation Authority (CAA), one can also learn how to make a claim or report an unlicenced operator.

A must-visit site for anyone looking for a refund on a trip that did not deliver. Don't get mad, get even by reporting the company and filing a claim!

www.abta.com
The Association of British Travel Agents

Overall rating: ★ ★ ★ ★			
Classification:	Information	**Readability:**	★ ★ ★
Updating:	Frequently	**Content:**	★ ★ ★
Navigation:	★ ★ ★	**Speed:**	★ ★ ★

UK

This site is ABTA's web directory providing users with information on 2300 UK member companies. It also offers information on the destinations each travel company features, and any special skills. Visitors can search the directory easily either by destination or specialisation specifics. By inputting either South Africa or Safari, for example, one can find out which travel agencies have tours, packages, or discounts to the wild kingdom experience. Site visitors can then ask the travel agency to send a brochure or simply ask to have more information on prices emailed to them. Other features include a holiday checklist that helps organise your trip from start to finish.

SPECIAL FEATURES

The site gives a telephone number so one can call and check that tour operators hold the proper licenses before booking a holiday. In addition, one can seek advice on travel contracts and ways to handle problems that may arise with the service offered by a specific company.

A great site for anyone planning a holiday with a relatively unknown tour operator.

www.festivals.com
Festivals

Overall rating: ★ ★ ★			
Classification:	Listings	**Readability:**	★ ★ ★ ★
Updating:	Frequently	**Content:**	★ ★ ★ ★
Navigation:	★ ★ ★ ★	**Speed:**	★ ★ ★ ★

US

This site compiles information on festivals and events around the world including the day's Greatest Event. When we visited, it was the Cannes Film Festival. But other than providing the dates and where it was happening (Cannes!), this service offered little but a general number to phone for information. It is, however, a great directory for other services.

SPECIAL FEATURES

Music gives the dates, locations, and phone numbers for top musical events around the world from Bach to Jazz.

Kids shows the top 25 children's festivals coming up all over the world including the children's shrine visiting day in Japan, and the puppet festival in Germany. Also included is a cool page for kids to download, a bookstore on festivals, and a family fun page divided into furry events (animal shows) gross listings (like the worm race in California) and brainy events like science fairs.

OTHER FEATURES

Other categories include art shows, cultural events, motorsports, and sporty events from poker tournaments to rodeos. In each category there's a special feature on an interesting event that month.

A great site and service for what's on where!

OTHER SITES OF INTEREST

Mobal

www.mobalrental.com

This site provides a mobile phone rental service anywhere in the world where one's own mobile phone doesn't work. The site also tells whether or not a mobile phone network is compatible with the network in the country visited. If not, one can rent a mobile phone from this company online, sending details by email.

Book-a-limo worldwide

www.1800bookalimo.com

There is nothing nicer than disembarking after a long plane journey and seeing a man in a suit holding a card with your name ready on it, ready to sweep you into a limousine and drive you off to the hotel in comfort. This service offers everything from a three-hour sightseeing tour of Paris in a private car, limo or van for £200, to door-to-door service from your hotel in Venice to the airport for around £60. You can reserve cars online for services in cities all over the world, and for those who have not been lucky enough to travel in one, even see what the inside of a limousine looks like. Clients can watch TV and sip champagne while taking in the sights or recovering from the flight. Additional site features include weather, travel tips and currency exchange.

Internet Café Guide

www.netcafeguide.com

With more than 2900 cybercafés in 133 countries as of May 2000, one should be able to get online anywhere in the world. This site offers the ultimate list so one can find the perfect cybercafé, whether in Miami or Mozambique. With a purple background and bold orange graphics, it has the feel of a cool café. Sponsored by the author of the Internet Café Guide: Cybercaf(yellow pages, this site is fast and easy to use. Just name a town, and a list of internet caf(s comes up with the address, hours, types of computers, and even a brief description of what food and drink is available. The site also features a link to the internet personal ads so one can arrange to meet a date at the café. One can also find out the latest hotel discounts around the world including hotel rooms in New York that start at about £40 and learn about the hottest new cybercafé in the world where one can read the Cybercafé news.

Dogs Away

www.dogsaway

A great site for anyone who likes to take their furry friend on holiday. As cat and dog owners can now buy a pet passport that will enable them to take Fido or Fifi out of the UK without subjecting them to quarantine upon return, this site is extremely helpful and timely.

Chapter 7

just for fun

'Words are, of course, the most powerful drug used by mankind.'

Rudyard Kipling (1923)

Travelogues, Articles and Features

Whether you're reading to obtain information about a specific region, or just for fun, the following travelogues will provide a comprehensive insight. Nothing can be more informative sometimes than the personal experiences of fellow travellers.

You might also be lucky enough to find a feature covering a special interest of yours — if you do, read it. Such features can be the most informative sources on the web.

www.travelmag.co.uk
Travelmag

Overall rating: ★ ★ ★ ★ ★			
Classification: Ezine		Readability:	★ ★ ★ ★
Updating: Monthly		Content:	★ ★ ★ ★
Navigation: ★ ★ ★ ★ ★		Speed:	★ ★ ★ ★ ★

UK

This eclectic monthly web magazine has a casual approach to its easy-to-use content. The very simple (got to love it!) homepage presents a letter from the editor confessing that Travelmag includes some of the best and worst travel writing on the web. It's best to click on Links, which takes you to a great gateway page called Webwide, and then scroll down to see the categories available.

SPECIAL FEATURES

Magazines links to a number of web travel magazines, such as the Expedia (see p. 41) magazine and Lonely Planet's magazine. It's one of the easiest ways to search a number of publications for coverage of a particular subject in a very short time.

Travel Diaries presents a number of travelogues indexed by subject. They all make for interesting reading, although they vary greatly in their perspective, from that of a backpacker to an executive travelling the globe in seats at the very, very front of the plane.

All in all, a site with very interesting and diverse content.

http://travel.roughguides.com/spotlight
Rough Guides

Overall rating: ★ ★ ★ ★ ★			
Classification:	Guides	Readability:	★ ★ ★ ★
Updating:	Monthly	Content:	★ ★ ★ ★
Navigation:	★ ★ ★ ★ ★	Speed:	★ ★ ★ ★ ★

UK

www.concierge.com
Concierge

Overall rating: ★ ★ ★ ★ ★			
Classification:	Ezine	Readability:	★ ★ ★ ★ ★
Updating:	Daily	Reliability:	★ ★ ★ ★ ★
Navigation:	★ ★ ★ ★	Speed:	★ ★ ★ ★

US

One of the most important aspects of searching for travelogues has got to be the size of the archive. It's no good having the most artistic and articulately written travelogue in the world if it's not on the subject you're after. This is where the Rough Guides Spotlight site succeeds. The archive is huge, and there are a number of easy ways to search it.

On the right-hand side of the Spotlight page, there's an index of continents linking to pages in the archives. You're then presented with a lengthy list of articles available for reading.

Each month a different region is selected as the topic for the Spotlight and excerpts from the printed guidebooks can be found on the homepage. Sometimes even more interesting however, are the Related Links which cover some of the most unusual details about the regions.

Most of the Rough Guide's logues are written by people travelling on a small budget, so they are perfect for those interested in tips on economising.

Click on the CNTraveler icon in the top left-hand corner of the Concierge homepage to find the many brilliant articles featured in Condé Nast's Traveller magazine, all of which appear to direct themselves at the glamorous traveller. There are many interesting Top or Gold List reports covering topics such as Ski and Golf Resorts, Spas, and World's Best Beaches. The content of the magazine makes for a super evening's read in itself, whether plans for travel are in the making or not. (See also p. 53.)

OTHER SITES OF INTEREST

Let's Go
www.letsgo.com
Monthly magazine on the web. Yellow Jacket for the budget traveller.

Journeywoman
www.journeywoman.com
(see p. 99)

Newspapers

Some of the best travel information in the English language is produced in British and American national newspapers. The following sites are dynamic with easy-to-use search facilities, and provide some of the highest quality information on the web, for both holiday and business travellers.

www.nytimes.com
New York Times Travel

Overall rating: ★ ★ ★ ★

Classification:	Information	**Readability:**	★ ★ ★ ★ ★
Updating:	Daily	**Content:**	★ ★ ★ ★ ★
Navigation:	★ ★ ★ ★ ★	**Speed:**	★ ★ ★ ★ ★

US R

One of the best sources of travel information around, covering all aspects of travel from destination information, to chat room forums, to a massive archive of anything related to travel. Of course, all the articles are targeted at the North American traveller, but many people from all around the world use this site for reliable information. Registration is required to visit the Travel section, but this is a very brief ordeal, requiring name, password, and other personal details.

On New York Times homepage, you'll find the Travel category listed in the site index on the left-hand side of the screen. The Travel page is fairly easy to decipher, but ignore the misleading titles, such as site index and marketplace, in black boxes under the page title. These are not relevant to the travel page, but are intended as navigation aids for the entire New York Times. Instead, scroll down to find your area of interest.

Primarily aimed at the American traveller, though there's still plenty of interest for those who are UK-based

www.the-planet.co.uk
Planet

Overall rating: ★ ★ ★ ★ ★			
Classification:	Information	**Readability:**	★ ★ ★ ★ ★
Updating:	Regularly	**Content:**	★ ★ ★ ★
Navigation:	★ ★ ★ ★ ★	**Speed:**	★ ★ ★ ★ ★

UK

This is an electronic Telegraph production, which presents an online archive of travel articles from the Telegraph newspaper. The most popular and useful category on the rather slick homepage is the Travel Article Search, which allows one to fill in a keyword, or use scroll-down Region or Activity menus. The wealth of information available is amazing, and a real plus is that these articles are directed at the British traveller.

SPECIAL FEATURES

Guided Tours leads to a very un-Telegraph-like page called Departure Lounge, where there are cartoon images of many different types of tour guides, ranging from middle-aged and elderly couples to footloose and fancy-free singles. The visitor then clicks on their likenesses to display their passports. The different tour guides have been travelling in different parts of the globe and their reports are informative and well written. The idea and presentation are amusing, even though on the day of review not all the images seemed to work. Also, why out of all 12 of the tour guides do none of them have children? Could the Planet site editor be anti-family?

An absolutely fantastic site... a must to dot the I's and cross the T's on any trip.

OTHER SITES OF INTEREST

The Sunday Times Travel
www.sunday-times.co.uk/travel/

The Guardian
www.guardian.co.uk/travel/

Graphics and Pictures

Although still developing, the graphics on the following sites can give insight that words sometimes just can't. The graphics featured on some of the African and Asian destination sites, listed in Chapter One, are also worth a look.

As well as being informative the pictures on the graphic sites make for great homemade egreetings cards or screen savers for avid travellers.

www.ipicture.co.uk
ipicture

Overall rating: ★ ★ ★ ★

Classification:	Graphics	**Readability:**	★ ★ ★ ★
Updating:	Regularly	**Reliability:**	★ ★ ★ ★
Navigation:	★ ★ ★ ★ ★	**Speed:**	★ ★ ★

UK

Ipicture offers travellers a growing library of multimedia products organised in an easy-to-search system. Included in the library are pictures, video clips, and many other features, which are all designed to help choose places to go. The pictures and videos are a combination of professional and amateur efforts.

SPECIAL FEATURES

Video Click on the camera icon on the world map, wait for the plug-ins to load, then choose a location. Some fairly rough video clips of the location chosen will appear, but so far the choice is limited, for example only Milan and Sicily are included for Italy. And you do have to wait an awfully long time for the clips that are there to appear.

Photos presents an exhaustive directory of pictures indexed by country, region, and then subject matter. A search under Nice, France presents ten pages of various images. It can be a very pleasant way to plan what to see on a visit.

Time Travel is a library of images dating back to the 1960s. Even exotic locations change, and rapidly if these pictures are anything to go by.

When the text gets too dense on some sites, shift to this for a novel way of learning about destinations. There's a great travel site search facility too!

OTHER SITES OF INTEREST

Terraquest
www.terraquest.com
This site presents virtual images of three expeditions to Antarctica, the Galapagos Islands, and a climbing journey in Yosemite National Park. If these regions are of interest to you, this is a worthwhile site.

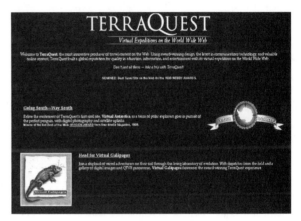

iPIX
www.ipix.com/travel/gallery/index.shtml
This site demonstrates how travel sites will be able to take you on a virtual tour of the accommodation before you even book.

Newsgroups

There are endless forums, newsgroups and bulletin boards (different terms for much the same thing) on the web. Most of them are filled with people typing in varying degrees of nonsense, which doesn't inspire newcomers to join in. However, you shouldn't completely dismiss these resources. As long as you bear in mind that the information you receive may vary in the degree of reliability, they can be be a great source of information. You could be looking through guide books and travel diaries for hours trying to answer a specific question such as 'which days is the market in San Remo, Italy, in operation?' Send in the query to an appropriate bulletin board and you'll probably get a reliable response within an hour or so. Of course, you don't always get an answer, but for the minimal effort it takes it is worth a try.

How to use newsgroups and messageboards

Messageboards function in the same way as an old-fashioned noticeboard or newsagents' window: you post a notice or question on a virtual noticeboard and wait for replies.

You can email your query or contribution to a designated address and then log on to the noticeboard to view further developments. In some cases you can have the responses emailed straight back to you.

Accessing newsgroups

The Usenet network of newsgroups is vast, and most British internet service providers will subscribe to several thousand of the total available. Other ISPs, for example AOL and Compuserve, have newsgroups that are accessible only by

their own subscribers. Many of the sites mentioned in this guide also have links to forums of related topics.

If you have never subscribed to a Usenet newsgroup before you will need to set up your browser or install special newsreader software. The set-up process varies depending on the type of browser you have, and the particular version. You will eventually be presented with a never-ending list, or a search facility where you can input 'travel' or 'wine' to find groups on those subjects.

The names and addresses of newsgroups look a bit odd. Newsgroups are divided into channels, so that people with common interests can exchange messages. These can be identified by abbreviations such as 'rec'. for recreation or 'sci.' for science and technology. Each channel might be further sub-divided into more specific subjects such as rec.travel.caribbean or rec.food.italian. Once a forum is found that looks as though it may be interesting, click on the OK button and your browser will automatically subscribe to it. Newsgroups then show up as a category or folder along with email folders such as Inbox, Unsent Messages and now Newshost. From there, sending and receiving messages to newsgroups operates just in the same way as sending and receiving email.

Another method to locate a newgroup or discussion group is to use the www.dejanews.com discussion search facility. This will link you to groups not necessarily subscribed to by your ISP. Alternatively you can enter rec.travel or a similar string into a search engine such as altavista.co.uk, or google.com.

Alt.travel and rec.travel, which are both divided into loads of subcategories such as alt.travel.canada or alt.travel.europe, have some newsgroups that are useful, articulate and a pleasure to use. Some others, of course, can vary depending on the topic. Look out for 'moderated' groups, which tend to be better pruned and more polite.

You can ask the most detailed question, such as where to park a car or buy the best local foods for self-catering. But as a newcomer to a discussion, beware of asking very obvious questions; the regular users can be scathing in their response to 'newbies' who ask an old chestnut that they've heard hundreds of times before. Many groups have a Frequently Asked Questions section (FAQs), and you'd do well to check here first to see if your enquiry has already been dealt with. You should also read the group's 'charter', or set of rules they agree to abide by to avoid an unwitting breech of etiquette.

Chat rooms

On certain websites you can converse with others in real time, rather than posting a question or observation and waiting for a response. But the conversation is only as stimulating as the people online when you log in and all too often descends into banality or innuendo. Try searching for 'chat travel' using your favourite search engine to find suitable sites.

Mailing lists

In these groups, the questions and answers are circulated by email to everyone who has signed up to the mailing list. They are often more polite and helpful than newsgroups (certainly there's less name calling in evidence), though finding a suitable group is not always easy. To find a relevant list, type something like '"mailing list" travel Himalayas' into a search engine. Don't forget to unsubscribe from a list when you're going away though, or you'll come back to thousands of unread messages.

Glossary of Internet Terms

A

Accelerators Add-on programs, which speed up browsing.

Acceptable Use Policy These are the terms and conditions of using the internet. They are usually set by organisations who wish to regulate an individual's use of the internet. For example, an employer might issue a ruling on the type of email which can be sent from an office.

Access Provider A company which provides access to the internet, usually via a dial-up account. Many companies such as AOL and Dircon charge for this service, although there are an increasing number of free services such as Freeserve, Lineone and Tesco.net. Also known as an Internet Service Provider.

Account A user's internet connection, with an Access/Internet Service Provider, which usually has to be paid for.

Acrobat Reader Small freely-available program, or web browser plug-in, which lets you view a Portable Document Format (PDF) file.

Across Lite Plug-in which allows you to complete crossword puzzles online.

Address Location name for email or internet site, which is the online equivalent of a postal address. It is usually composed of a unique series of words and punctuation, such as *my.name@myhouse.co.uk*. See also URL.

America Online (AOL) World's most heavily subscribed online service provider.

Animated GIF Low-grade animation technique used on websites.

ASCII Stands for American Standard Code for Information Interchange, It is a coding standard which all computers can recognise, and ensures that if a character is entered on one part of the internet, the same character will be seen elsewhere.

ASCII Art Art made of letters and other symbols. Because it is made up of simple text, it can be recognised by different computers.

ASDL Stands for Asynchronous Digital Subscriber Line, which is a high speed copper wire which will allow rapid transfer of information. Not widely in use at moment, though the government is pushing for its early introduction.

Attachment A file included with an email, which may be composed of text, graphics and sound. Attachments are encoded for transfer across the internet, and can be viewed in their original form by the recipient. An attachment is the equivalent of putting a photograph with a letter in the post.

B

Bookmark A function of the Netscape Netvigator browser which allows you to save a link to your favourite web pages, so that you can return straight there at a later date, without having to re-enter the address. Favourites in internet Explorer is the same thing.

BPS Abbreviation of Bits Per Second, which is a measure of the speed at which information is transferred or downloaded.

Browse Common term for looking around the web. See also Surfing.

Browser A generic term for the software that allows users to move and look around the Web. Netscape Navigator and

Internet Explorer are the ones that most people are familiar with, and they account for 97 percent of web hits.

Bulletin Board Service A BBS is a computer with a telephone connection, which allows you direct contact to upload and download information and converse with other users, via the computer. It was the forerunner to the online services and virtual communities of today.

C

Cache A temporary storage space on the hard drive of your computer, which stores downloaded websites. When you return to a website, information is retrieved from the cache and displayed much more rapidly. However, this information may not be the most recent version for sites which are frequently updated and you will need to reload the Website address for these.

Chat Talking to other users on the web in real time, but with typed, instead of spoken words. Special software such as ICQ or MIRC is required before you can chat.

Chat Room An internet channel which allows several people to type in their messages, and talk to one another over the internet.

Clickstream The trail left as you 'click' your way around the web.

Content The material on a website that actually relates to the site, and is hopefully of interest or value. Things like adverts are not considered to be part of the content. The term is also used to refer to information on the internet that can be seen by users, as opposed to programming and other background information.

Cookie A cookie is a nugget of information sometimes sent by websites to your hard drive when you visit. They contain such details as what you looked at, what you ordered, and can add more information, so that the website can be customized to suit you.

Cybercafe Cafe where you can use a computer terminal to browse the net for a small fee.

Cyberspace When first coined by the sci-fi author William Gibson, it meant a shared hallucination which occured when people logged on to computer networks. Now, it refers to the virtual space you're in when on the internet.

D

Dial Up A temporary telephone connection to your ISP's computer and how you make contact with your ISP, each time you log onto the Internet.

Domain The part of an Internet address which identifies an individual computer, and can often be a business or person's name. For example, in the goodwebguide.com the domain name is theGoodWebGuide.

Download Transfer of information from an Internet server to your computer.

Dynamic HTML The most recent version of the HTML standard.

E

Ecash Electronic cash, used to make transactions on the internet.

Ecommerce The name for business which is carried out over the internet.

Email Mail which is delivered electronically over the internet. They are usually comprised of text messages, but can contain illustrations, music and animations. Mail is sent to an email address, which is the internet equivalent of a postal address.

Encryption A process whereby information is scrambled to produce a 'coded message', so that it can't be read whilst in transit on the internet. The recipient must have decryption software in order to read the message.

Expire Term referring to newsgroup postings which are automatically deleted after a fixed period of time.

Ezine Publication on the web, which is updated regularly.

F

FAQ Stands for frequently asked questions and is a common section on websites where the most common enquiries and their answers are archived.

Frame A method which splits web pages into several windows.

FTP/File Transfer Protocol Standard method for transporting files across the internet.

G

GIF/Graphics Interchange Format A format in which graphics are compressed, and a popular method of putting images onto the internet, as they take little time to download.

Gopher The gopher was the precursor of the world wide web and consisted of archives accessed through a menu, usually organised by subject.

GUI/Graphical User Interface. This is the system which turns binary information into the words and images format you can see on your computer screen. For example, instead of seeing the computer language which denotes the presence of your toolbar, you actually see a toolbar.

H

Hackers A term used to refer to expert programmers who used their skills to break into computer systems, just for the fun of it. Nowadays the word is more commonly associated with computer criminals, or Crackers.

Header Basic indication of what's in an email: who it's from, when it was sent, and what it's about.

Hit When a file is downloaded from a website it is referred to as a 'hit'. Measuring the number of hits is a rough method of counting how many people visit a website. Except that it's not wholly accurate as one website can contain many files, so one visit by an individual may generate several hits.

Homepage Most usually associated with a personal site, produced by an individual, but can also refer to the first page on your browser, or the first page of a website.

Host Computer on which a website is stored. A host computer may store several websites, and usually has a fast powerful connection to the internet. Also known as a Server.

HTML/Hypertext Mark-Up Language The computer code used to construct web pages.

HTTP/Hypertext Transfer Protocol The protocol for moving HTML files across the web.

Hyperlink A word or graphic formatted so that when you click on it, you move from one area to another. See also hypertext.

Hypertext Text within a document which is formatted so it acts as a link from one page to another, or from one document to another.

I

Image Map A graphic which contains hyperlinks.

Interface What you actually see on the computer screen.

Internet One or more computers connected to one another is an internet (lower case i). The Internet is the biggest of all the internets. and consists of a worldwide collection of interconnected computer networks.

Internet Explorer One of the most popular pieces of browser software, produced by Microsoft.

Intranet A network of computers, which works in the same way as an internet, but for internal use, such as within a corporation.

ISDN/Integrated Services Digital Network Digital telephone line which facilitates very fast connections and can transfer larges amounts of data. It can carry more than one form of data at once.

ISP/Internet Service Provider See Access Provider.

J

Java Programming language which can be used to create interactive multimedia effects on webpages. The language is used to create programmes known as *applets* that add features such as animations, sound and even games to websites.

Javascript A scripting language which, like Java, can be used to add extra multimedia features. However, in contrast with Java it does not consist of separate programmes. Javascript is embedded into the HTML text and can interpreted by the browser, provided that the user has a javascript enabled browser.

JPEG Stands for 'Joint Photographic Experts Group' and is the name given to a type of format which compresses photos, so that they can be seen on the web.

K

Kill file A function which allows a user to block incoming information from unwanted sources. Normally used on email and newsreaders.

L

LAN/Local Area Network A type of internet, but limited to a single area, such as an office.

Link Connection between web pages, or one web document and another, which are accessed via formatted text and graphic.

Login The account name or password needed to access a computer system.

M

Mailing List A discussion group which is associated with a website. Participants send their emails to the site, and it is copied and sent by the server to other individuals on the mailing list.

Modem A device for converting digital data into analogue signals for transmission along standard phone lines. The usual way for home users to connect to the internet or log into their email accounts. May be internal (built into the computer) or external (a desk-top box connected to the computer).

MP3 A compressed music file format, which has almost no loss of quality although the compression rate may be very high.

N

Netscape Popular browser, now owned by AOL.

Newbie Term for someone new to the Internet. Used perjoratively of newcomers to bulletin boards or chat, who commit the sin of asking obvious questions or failing to observe the netiquette.

Netiquette The system of manners that exists for conversing across the internet, or sending email.

Newsgroup Discussion group amongst Internet users who share a mutual interest. There are thousands of newsgroups covering every possible subject.

O

Offline Not connected to the internet via a telephone line.

Online Connected to the internet via a telephone line.

Offline Browsing A function of the browser software, which allows the user to download pages and read them whilst offline.

Online Service Provider Similar to an access provider, but provides additional features such as live chat.

P

PDF/Portable Document Format A file format created by Adobe for offline reading of brochures, reports and other documents with complex graphic design, which can be read by anyone with Acrobat Reader.

Plug-in Piece of software which adds more functions (such as playing music or video) to another, larger software program.

POP3/Post Office Protocol An email protocol that allows you to pick up your mail from any location on the web.

Portal A website which offers many services, such as search engines, email and chat rooms, and to which people are likely to return to often. ISPs such as Yahoo and Alta Vista provide portal sites which are the first thing you see when you log on, and in theory act as gateways to the rest of the web.

Post/Posting Information sent to a usenet group, bulletin board, message board or by email.

PPP/Point to Point Protocol The agreed way of sending data over dial-up connections, so that the user's computer, the modem and the Internet Server can all recognise it. It is the protocol which allows you to get online.

Protocol Convention detailing a set of actions that computers in a network must follow so that they can understand one another.

Q

Query Request for specific information from a database.

R

RAM /Random Access Memory Your computer's short term memory.

Realplayer A plug-in program that allows you to view video in real-time and listen to sound and which is becoming increasingly important for web use.

Router A computer program which acts as an interface between two networks, and decides how to route information.

S

Searchable Database A database on a website which allows the user to search for information, usually by keyword.

Search Engine Programs which enable web users to search for pages and sites using keywords. They are usually to be found on portal sites and browser homepages. Infoseek, Alta Vista and Lycos are some of the popular search engines.

Secure Transactions Information transfers which are encrypted so that only the sender and recipient have access to the uncoded message, so that the details within remain private. The term is most commonly used to refer to credit card transactions, although other information can be sent in a secure form.

Server A powerful computer that has a permanent fast connection to the internet. Such computers are usually owned by companies and act as host computers for websites.

Sign-on To connect to the internet and start using one of its facilities.

Shareware Software that doesn't have to be paid for or test version of software that the user can access for free, as a trial before buying it.

Standard A style which the whole of the computer industry has agreed upon. Industry standards mean that hardware and software produced by the various different computer companies will work with one another.

Surfing Slang for looking around the Internet, without any particular aim, following links from site to site.

T

TLA/Three Letter Acronyms Netspeak for the abbreviations of net jargon, such as BPS (Bits Per Second) and ISP (Internet Service Provider).

U

Upload To send files from your computer to another one on the internet. When you send an email you are uploading a file.

URL/Uniform Resource Locator Jargon for an address on the internet, such as www.thegoodwebguide.co.uk.

Usenet A network of newsgroups, which form a worldwide system, on which anyone can post 'news'.

V

Virtual Community Name given to a congregation of regular mailing list/ newsgroup users.

VRML/Virtual Reality Modelling Language Method for creating 3D environments on the web.

W

Wallpaper Description of the sometimes hectic background patterns which appear behind the text on some websites.

Web Based Email/Webmail Email accounts such as Hotmail and Rocketmail, which are accessed via an Internet browser, rather than an email program such as Outlook Express. Webmail has to be typed whilst the user is online, but can be accessed from anywhere on the Web.

Webmaster A person responsible for a web server. May also be known as System Administrator.

Web Page Document which forms one part of a website (though some sites are a single page), usually formatted in HTML.

Web Ring Loose association of websites which are usually dedicated to the same subject and often contain links to one another.

Website A collection of related web pages which often belong to an individual or organisation and are about the same subject.

World Wide Web The part of the Internet which is easy to get around and see. The term is often mistakely interchanged with Internet, though the two are not the same. If the Internet is a shopping mall, with shops, depots, and delivery bays, then the web is the actual shops which the customers see and use.

Index

Other great titles in thegoodwebguide series:

Money	Gardening	Food	Parents
ISBN 1-903282-02-0	ISBN 1-903282-00-4	ISBN 1-903282-01-2	ISBN 1-903282-03-9

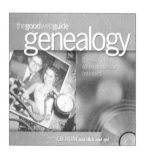   

Genealogy	Travel	Wine	Health
ISBN 1-903282-06-3	ISBN 1-903282-05-5	ISBN 1-903282-04-7	ISBN 1-903282-08-X